Dementia and Psychotherapy Reconsidered

Richard Cheston

Open University Press

Open University Press
McGraw Hill
Unit 4,
Foundation Park
Roxborough Way
Maidenhead
SL6 3UD

email: emea_uk_ireland@mheducation.com
world wide web: www.openup.co.uk

First edition published 2022

A catalogue record of this book is available from the British Library

ISBN-13: 9780335250981
ISBN-10: 033525098X
eISBN: 9780335250998

Library of Congress Cataloging-in-Publication Data
CIP data applied for

Typeset by Transforma Pvt. Ltd., Chennai, India

Praise Page

"Rik Cheston is one of the pioneers of psychotherapy in dementia. This book integrates his clinical expertise and research, and is brought vividly to life by Rik's personal reflections and case examples drawn from his vast experience. Dementia and Psychotherapy Reconsidered addresses how can we help people with dementia to talk about what is happening to them and highlights the importance of including families in these conversations. Rik doesn't shy away from the challenges of undertaking psychotherapy with people with dementia and thoughtfully considers factors that can complicate therapy from both the clinician's and the client's perspectives.

Rik describes himself as "unashamedly eclectic" (as all the best therapists are), and as such his book doesn't privilege a specific therapeutic modality. As a clinical psychologist, this book will be one that I keep coming back to and share with my trainees. It has relevance to many areas of dementia care because of its focus on being therapeutic as well as delivering therapy."

Dr Emma Wolverson, Clinical Psychologist. Senior Lecturer in
Ageing and Dementia. Research Lead Dementia UK

"After the bombshell of receiving a diagnosis of dementia, people with dementia and those close to them struggle with two competing instincts – to carry on as if nothing has changed or to acknowledge and deal with their new reality. In this brilliant and timely book, Richard Cheston maps the conflict between these two 'voices' and how we can help people to resolve it by finding ways to talk about dementia and how they experience it. Cheston draws upon the literature, his own research and over 30 years of insightful clinical practice to discuss not only psychotherapy but a whole lot more. The book is lucidly written so can be valuable not only to specialists but to anyone whose work or personal life brings them into contact with dementia. Actually, that's most of us."

Tom Dening, Professor of Dementia Research, Mental Health &
Clinical Neurosciences, University of Nottingham, UK

"This is a thoughtful and, at times, provocative book, providing knowledge and insights from theoretical and practical perspectives. Cheston provides a very good account of an unwieldly area, providing theory and clinical observations hand-in-hand. This is a really helpful methodology because some of the concepts are best illustrated with practical examples.

The book is well structured, with four parts. There is a clear introduction and summary at the end of every part and also within each chapter.

The work is not a detailed review of the literature, rather the author has 'woven in' some key frameworks with his own extensive experience. Indeed, the best chapters are those where he discusses examples from his own service or team; the chapter on group psychotherapy is a good example this.

The book is in keeping with the 'Dementia Reconsidered' tradition, challenging the reader's perspective ensuring that we check our biases and assumptions in terms of our approaches and interactions with people living with dementia. For example, Cheston discusses existential threats and biopsychosocial ideas, asking continuously "... where does the 'person' reside in all of this". He challenges us to be less vague and to sharpen-up our perspectives. One of my favourite chapters is entitled 'Finding distance and perspective', it calls upon us to be cautious about how we speak to people living with dementia about the nature of dementia. This is a roller coaster of a chapter which discusses education, stigma, shame and the consistency and measurement of insight.

I recommend this book. However, like other authors in the series, Cheston has set out to challenge you; which he does extremely well."

Professor Ian Andrew James, Innovations Team, CNTW NHS Trust and honorary professor at the University of Bradford, UK

"This thoughtful text on psychotherapy and dementia provides wonderful explanations in plain English of complex theories about why we react as we do to existential threat, about how talking can help and about how psychotherapy can assist people living with dementia. The author joins the dots between scientific understanding, clinical practice and lived experience in a consummate, compassionate way, resulting in a book that is a 'must read'. Everyone involved in delivering psychotherapeutic care to those living with dementia should have it on their shelf."

Jan R Oyebode, Professor of Dementia Care, Centre for Applied Dementia Studies, University of Bradford, UK

"This is a clear, accessible and beautifully written legacy of psychotherapeutic endeavour in dementia care. The author shows how we as human beings in relationship with the person living with a dementia, can work with the ongoing existential challenges of the condition, using what is most helpful from a range of psychotherapeutic approaches. The chapters offer a deeply empathic knowledgebase, including embracing cultural aspects such as within South Asian communities. This book is a seminal text for all who are committed to continually improving their practice in person-centred dementia care."

Esme Moniz-Cook Professor Emerita (Clinical Psychology, Ageing and Dementia Care), University of Hull, UK.
Founder Chair, now board member INTERDEM

Titles in the series

Dementia and Psychotherapy, Richard Cheston

Forthcoming Titles

Education and training in dementia care: A Person-centred Approach, Claire Surr, Sarah Jane Smith and Isabelle Latham

Reconsidering Ethics in Dementia Care, Julian Hughes

Reconsidering Leisure and Dementia, Christopher Russell, Jane Twigg and Karen Gray (eds)

Neighbourhoods and the Lived Experience of Dementia: Spaces, Places and People, John Keady (ed)

Talking with Dementia, Reconsidered, Keith Oliver, Reinhard Guss and Ruth Bartlett

Contents

Preface

Preface for the *Reconsidering Dementia* book series for *Dementia and Psychotherapy Reconsidered*

Series Editors: Dawn Brooker and Keith Oliver

The dementia field has developed rapidly in its scope and practice over the past 25 years. Many thousands of people are diagnosed with dementia each year. Worldwide, the trend is that people are being diagnosed at much earlier stages. In addition, families and friends increasingly provide support to those affected by dementia over a prolonged period. Many people, both those diagnosed with dementia and those who support them, have an appetite to understand their condition. Care professionals and civic society also need an in-depth and nuanced understanding of how to support people living with dementia within their communities over the long term.

The *Reconsidering Dementia* book series sets out to address this need. It takes its inspiration from the late Professor Tom Kitwood's seminal text *Dementia Reconsidered* published in 1997 which, at the time, revolutionized how dementia care was conceptualized. The book series editors worked together on the 2nd Edition of the book entitled *Dementia Reconsidered, Revisited: The Person Still Comes First.* This 2019 publication was a reprint of the original text by Tom Kitwood alongside contemporary commentaries for each chapter written by current experts. Many topics in the field of dementia care, however, were simply unheard of in Kitwood's lifetime. The subsequent titles in this series are cutting-edge scholarly texts that challenge and engage readers to think deeply. They draw on theoretical understandings, contemporary research and experience to critically reflect on their topic in great depth.

This does not mean, however, that they are not applicable to improving the care and support to those affected by dementia. As well as the scholarly text, all books have a 'So what?' thread that unpacks what this means for people living with dementia, their families, people working in dementia care, policy makers, professionals, community activists, and so on. Too many books either focus on an academic audience **or** a practitioner audience **or** a student audience **or** a lived experience audience. In this series, the aim is to try to address these perspectives in the round. The *Reconsidering Dementia* book series attempts to bring together the perspectives of professional practice, scholarship and the lived experience as they pertain to the key topics in the field of dementia studies.

The book series is jointly commissioned and edited by Professor Dawn Brooker MBE and by Dr Keith Oliver. Dawn has been active in the field of dementia care since the 1980s as a clinician and an academic. She draws on her experience and international networks to bring together a series of books on the most pertinent issues in the field. Keith is one of the foremost international advocates for those living with dementia. He also brings an insightful perspective of his own and others' experience of what it means to live with dementia gained since his diagnosis of Alzheimer's disease in 2010.

One of the first titles Dawn and Keith wanted to commission was this book on *Dementia and Psychotherapy Reconsidered*. Kitwood himself was a psychotherapist and he articulated a psychological model of the experience of dementia. However, in Kitwood's lifetime the idea that people experiencing dementia could engage directly with talking therapies was unheard of. Rik Cheston was one of the pioneers of talking therapies in the field of dementia care in the UK and this book bears testament to Rik's vast experience within this field. This is a ground-breaking book that brings together know-how, scholarship and humanity in equal measure for all those engaged in talking with people about the experience of living with dementia.

Additional Thoughts from Keith Oliver

It has been an honour and a privilege for me as a person living with dementia to fulfil the role of co-editor for Rik Cheston's book, and from page one I was drawn in and hooked by Rik's wisdom, experience and style of writing. Since sharing my brain with Alzheimer's disease I have had many good days and weeks, but frustration and challenge is never far away, lurking in what I describe as the fog of my dementia. What Rik does is offer a pathway out of the fog into a sunnier place, one which I do know works. For half of the period since being diagnosed I have received therapy – either on the NHS or sourcing it myself privately – which has included psychotherapy, behaviour support therapy, and the two which worked best in a person-centred approach for me, which were narrative therapy and compassion-focused therapy. My sincere, heartfelt wish is that this book serves as a driving force to ensure more people with dementia are able to access good quality, person-centred therapy. It does work – I am living proof of this!

Acknowledgements

All psychotherapists learn from their clients. I am no exception. I'd therefore like to thank the many people with dementia, their families and friends with whom I worked during my time as a clinical psychologist working within Avon and Wiltshire Mental Health Partnership (NHS) Trust, and at the RICE memory clinic in Bath. Without their bravery in trusting me to talk about dementia and their willingness to share their experiences, I could not have begun to write this book. I hope that they feel I have been able to communicate some of that learning here.

I could not have envisaged, taken on, or completed this book without the support of my family: Andrea whose patient advice, support and proofreading was matched by her tolerance for my regular absence from our life; and Katharine and Huw who have kept me grounded by just being themselves.

I am grateful to Dawn Brooker and Keith Oliver, the series editors, for their encouragement. Not only did their enthusiasm for this project help me to feel that this book would be worthwhile, but their advice and comments on successive drafts have shaped its structure and contents. Keith's support has been especially validating for me, as his experiences of psychotherapy, and especially Compassion Focused Therapy, played such an important role in helping him to adjust to his illness.

Two very different psychologists whose work I have admired equally for many years, also read and commented on earlier drafts of the book: the eminent social psychologist Steven Sabat and the committed clinical psychologist, Suzanne Davis. I'd like to thank them both for their encouragement and advice.

I am one of a number of clinical psychologists who are active in person-centered dementia research in the UK and whose research integrates high levels of clinical expertise with strong academic skills and knowledge. They include Andrew Balfour, Mike Bender, Georgina Charlesworth, Jane Fossey, Polly Kaiser, Louisa Jackman, Ian James, Esme Moniz-Cook, Aimee Spector, Bob Woods and, of course, the wonderful Dawn Brooker. Over the years our paths have regularly crossed, often during events hosted by the British Psychological Society's Faculty of Psychology of Older People. Not only has their research influenced me directly, but their success in showing that clinical psychologists have an important contribution to make to research has been inspiring.

I have been fortunate to work with many passionate and committed colleagues over the last 30 years. They have acted in various capacities as my managers, co-workers, collaborators, peers, friends, students and trainees. They include many excellent clinicians within various community mental health teams in Avon and Wiltshire Mental Health Partnership (NHS) Trust, and at the RICE memory clinic in Bath as well as academics and researchers at UWE Bristol and beyond. Among others they are Jeremy Allen, Elizabeth

Bartlett, Nick Bennians, Gillian Bebber, Stephany Bowen, David Childs, Gary
Christopher, Peter Clegg, Peter Coleman, Lorraine Conduit, Fiona Cramp, Eliz-
abeth Drew, Jane Fossey, Marie Gianelli, Julia Gifford, Jane Gilliard, Rebecca
Guhan, Julia Hecquet, Julian Hughes, Lynne Hopkinson, Sanda Ismail, Ada
Ivanecka, Charlie Jones, Kerry Jones, Roy Jones, Jo Keightley, Anna Lager-
dahl, Anna Littlechild, Alice Loyal, Jill Mann, Ann Marshall, Rosslyn Offord,
Chris Pawson, Gill Podger, Jane Powell, Elsa Schmidt, Constantine Sedikides,
Debbie Smith, John Spreadbury, Bill Stiles, Deirdre Sutton-Smith, Paul Whitby,
Tim Wildschut, Philippa Wilson and Liz Young. In particular I need to thank
Emily Dodd at UWE Bristol who has worked with me to develop LivDem and
many other projects.

Finally, I would like to recognize the organizations that have funded different aspects of my research: AWP Mental Health Partnership (NHS) Trust;
BNSSG Clinical Commissioning Group; the Mental Health Foundation; the
National Institute for Health Research; the Alzheimer's Society; Alzheimer's
Research UK; and the University of the West of England. The views that I have
expressed here are mine, and mine alone, and do not reflect the views of any of
these agencies.

Introduction

> 'What I'm asserting may at first seem to be surprising, paradoxical, counterin-
> tuitive. Psychotherapy with dementing persons? What an absurd and impractical
> idea! A bit of behaviour modification – yes, by all means. Some reality orienta-
> tion, of course. But these, as we all know, are not 'real' psychotherapy, which
> aims at bringing about profound and enduring changes within persons. 'Real'
> psychotherapy with demented persons? That surely is a contradiction in terms.
> For doesn't dementia, by definition, mean a permanent loss of mind, which is
> roughly equivalent to saying 'out of psychotherapeutic reach?'
>
> Tom Kitwood, 1990, p. 42

The title of this book reflects its origins in the 2019 republication of Tom Kitwood's landmark publication *Dementia Reconsidered: The Person Comes
First*. The new book, edited by Professor Dawn Brooker was titled *Dementia
Reconsidered, Revisited: The Person Still Comes First* and in it each of the nine
chapters from the original book were republished alongside a commentary
(Kitwood and Brooker, 2019). For eight of these chapters, the commentary was
written by a contemporary dementia researcher and reviewed the progress
that had been made in that area in the 20+ years since the publication of the
original book. In keeping with the underlying principles of person-centred
dementia care that Tom Kitwood had done so much to advocate, the ninth and
remaining chapter was accompanied by a commentary written jointly by Keith
Oliver (a man living with dementia) and Reinhard Guss (a clinical psychologist). Additionally, both a foreword and afterword were also written by two
women living with dementia: Christine Bryden and Kate Swaffer.

I was lucky enough to meet Tom Kitwood at the start of my career in the
early 1990s. Throughout my career, my own clinical and research work has,
like so many others, continued to draw inspiration from Tom's writings. However, when I started working with people with dementia, as a newly qualified
clinical psychologist, I had no great interest in working with older people, let
alone people living with dementia. I had applied for a post in this area largely for
personal rather than professional reasons as I wanted to live near Bath, and this
was the only job I could find. While I had ambitions to develop as a psychotherapist,
there seemed little opportunity to do this, as the work of clinical psychologists
with people living with dementia seemed to be confined to three areas: the
assessment of people with memory problems; the provision of support to their
families; and the delivery of training for the staff caring for them.

One of the important turning points for me at this stage was when my first
Older Adult Psychology manager, Jane Fossey, lent me a copy of a 1990 article
that Tom had written in the Newsletter of the Psychotherapy Section of the
British Psychological Society. The extract above comes from this article. Compared to his other publications at this time, in *Ageing and Society* – the journal

of the British Society of Gerontology – this was a small, almost incidental article in a relatively obscure newsletter. However, what I read helped me to see possibilities in my work that I had previously not been aware of. By this time, I was aware of Tom's espousal of person-centred care, but I had assumed this was confined to institutional care – so to come across not only arguments that it might be possible to use psychotherapy with people living with dementia, but also that there might be a moral imperative to do so was something of a revelation.

However, while Tom's work fired me with a belief that psychotherapy might be possible, I still did not know how to do so. I am now approaching the end of my professional career and have spent much of the time since then trying to work out the answer to this question. This book is my attempt to record some of what I have learnt.

This book is divided into four sections. In common with the other books in this series, at the end of each section I have provided a brief summary of the most salient points, together with an outline of the main implications for people living with dementia, family carers, therapists and dementia care workers.

In Part 1, I set out an overview of what is meant by the term dementia. Chapter 1 provides a summary of the syndrome of dementia, its prevalence and impact on families and society.

Chapter 2 continues to look at the impact of dementia, but extends this to frame dementia as a psychological threat. This chapter draws on the work I have carried out with colleagues at the University of the West of England in Bristol and Constantine Sedikides and Tim Wildschut who are social and personality psychologists from the Centre for Research and Identity at the University of Southampton. In this collaboration we have begun to translate a major paradigm from social psychology, the Terror Management Theory (Solomon et al., 2015), into dementia research. In so doing, we have tested a series of hypotheses around how people defend themselves against threatening information. Although our early research was largely laboratory based, we have recently begun to take the first steps towards translating our ideas into clinical interventions – a process we hope to continue in the next few years.

Chapter 3 argues that people living with dementia have all too often been left to respond to this threat on their own, as for many the sheer awfulness of dementia has been ignored. Instead, this chapter makes the case that we need to find a way to talk about their dementia with people – and that psychotherapy has an important role to play in this.

Part 2 also consists of three chapters and examines how individual therapy (Chapter 4), couples therapy (Chapter 5) and group therapy (Chapter 6) can be used with this client group. Each of these chapters presents some of the relevant research base but also draws on my own experiences as a clinician providing psychotherapy and as an active researcher. In order to illustrate the potential for psychotherapy I have included in each chapter one or more clinical cases drawn from my own practice. In order to protect the anonymity of my clients I have taken two measures: first by using pseudonyms and changing all personal details; and secondly by ensuring that each case study is a composite of two or sometimes more pieces of clinical work.

Part 3 consists of four chapters that look at an issue that has been missing from many psychotherapeutic accounts – that is to say, how we talk about dementia with people who are living with dementia. In my work I have come to see a capacity to talk about dementia as synonymous with adjustment – both in the sense of people finding the words to describe their dementia to themselves and within therapy, but also in their being able to tell other people.

Chapter 7 sets out how, in the absence of a psychological model that could describe this process of talking and adjusting, I have adapted a framework developed by Bill Stiles, who is Professor Emeritus in the Department of Psychology at Miami University in Ohio. In contrast to many of the theoretical frameworks that have been applied to studies of awareness in dementia care, Bill's assimilation model represents a person's ability to process threatening or problematic material as involving both cognitive and emotional factors. I have found this adapted assimilation model to be a useful research tool, and an invaluable clinical aid.

Chapter 8 then examines the initial stages of this process of assimilation, stages in which the difficult, problematic nature of dementia is at first pushed away before emerging in a disguised form, progressively heightening the person's emotional response. The task of the person with dementia is to put a name to their dementia without being emotionally overwhelmed by this.

Chapter 9 continues to chart the process of adjustment as the individual strives to find some distance and perspective from their dementia, for instance by exploring how its impact resonates with other aspects of their life.

The final chapter in this section of the book (Chapter 10) looks at instances of how some people living with dementia have been able to incorporate their dementia into their existing identity and to find ways of balancing living their lives well with being mindful of their diagnosis.

In the final section, Part 4, I turn to factors which can complicate the application of psychotherapeutic skills. For the first time, in Chapter 11, I will foreground the direct consequences of the neurological damage inherent in dementia, and how the resulting cognitive impairment impacts on the therapeutic process. In Chapter 12 I will examine the need for therapists to take into account both social and personal frailty in assessing whether, and if so then how, to offer psychotherapeutic work. Finally, Chapter 13 returns to a central theme in Kitwood's 1990 paper – that of the importance of being therapeutic in dementia care as well as doing therapy.

In writing this book, I have made some assumptions about who might be likely to read it. First, I have assumed that readers will have at least a passing familiarity with dementia – for instance either from working in dementia care themselves or witnessing someone close to them experience a form of dementia. Similarly, I have also assumed that the majority of readers will have a background in the psychological, psychotherapeutic or counselling professions. This is not so much a book about how to do psychotherapy, as a book about how to adapt psychotherapeutic practice to accommodate the differing demands of working with people who are living with dementia and their families.

This book also reflects at least two of my own beliefs about therapy, or perhaps it might be more accurate to say, my own biases about therapy.

Firstly, while I appreciate that there are distinctions to be drawn between terms such as 'psychotherapy', 'counselling' and 'psychological therapy', to my mind there are far more similarities between all of these than there are differences. As novelists and dramatists have known for millennia, we are all capable of changing ourselves, of seeing the world in a new way, of gaining perspective and distance from trauma. There is no reason, then, to see the work that is done within psychotherapy as being different in its entirety from that which occurs within other settings. Nevertheless, I can appreciate that for many, this blurring of distinctions may feel at best imprecise, and at worst positively careless.

Secondly, just as my own therapeutic practice is unashamedly eclectic, so is this book; I have not sought to privilege any single therapeutic modality. Thus, in common with many clinical psychologists, as part of my own professional development I have trained as a CBT therapist and also spent a year on an experiential group analytic psychotherapy course. Again, I know there will be many whose own practice is much more focused, and for whom there is little if anything to be gained from studying other ways of working. If this is the case for you, then I can only hope that you will find enough of substance here to help you to use your own skills in working with people with dementia. Ultimately, perhaps the best way to learn is to make your own mistakes.

The genesis of this book is firmly within person-centred care. Accordingly, the focal question that I seek to answer is one that is central to person-centred dementia care, but one that has been, I believe, all too often neglected: *'How can we help people living with dementia to talk about what is happening to them?'* After all, being able to put a name to the challenges that someone faces should, one would imagine, be essential to any truly person-centred encounter. However, in my experience, it is striking how often this very basic discussion is missing from what are otherwise excellent forms of service provision. Perhaps even more surprisingly, finding a way to talk about their dementia with clients is also all too often missing from accounts of psychotherapy and counselling in this area.

The reasons why this neglect of dementia is so widespread is something that I will engage with throughout this book. Put simply, however, the reason may be obvious: dementia is just too big and too frightening a topic to touch upon lightly. I suspect that for many healthcare professionals it is, frankly, something of a conversation stopper. They avoid raising the subject, because they don't want to upset their clients and because they fear they wouldn't know what to say if this happens. If I am correct, and this is how many experienced clinicians feel, then this conversational dilemma is likely to be even stronger for the families of the person with dementia. Indeed, I know from talking with many people who have been diagnosed with dementia, that they too are very aware of the difficulties associated with talking about their diagnosis.

If finding a way to bring dementia into the conversational room can be problematic, this does not mean that we should not find a way to do so. There are many good reasons for doing just this – not least because it is much harder to adjust to an illness, if the condition itself cannot be mentioned. At the same time, there may also be very good reasons for not putting a name to what the science fiction author Terry Pratchett referred to as the 'demon' of dementia (Pratchett, 2015). Consequently, throughout this book I will explore the reasons why we should, and sometimes why we should not, talk about dementia. By focusing on this issue, I am aware that while I am doing so primarily within the context of psychotherapy, it is also relevant to many, if not all other areas of dementia care. Whether a health or social care professional works in a memory clinic, an Alzheimer's café or in residential care, they will often need to find a way to bring some aspects of dementia into the conversation. Not only will almost everyone who works with people with dementia benefit from understanding how people adjust to or respond to their dementia, but I also believe that much of this book will also be relevant to many family caregivers and indeed for some people living with dementia themselves. Many of the skills and issues I outline in this book are applicable to contexts outside psychotherapy or counselling. You don't have to be a therapist or counsellor to talk with someone about their dementia.

I will finish by recounting another story from my early years as a clinical psychologist struggling to understand both what I could do with people with dementia and what I should try to do. I attended two training sessions on what was at that time a novel, and somewhat controversial, therapeutic intervention: validation therapy (which I will briefly describe in Chapter 11). The first training session was in London and was led by Naomi Feil – the creator of this approach. Although I was intrigued by the possibility that talking to people with dementia and making an imaginative leap into their world might be helpful, I was also left somewhat bemused by much of the unfamiliarity of her approach.

Some months later I then attended another training session, also on Validation Therapy, led by the British clinical psychologist Bob Woods. After outlining the essence of Feil's approach, Bob seemed to sense the uncertainty in the room. He summarized his thoughts (and here I paraphrase these) by saying that the important thing was not whether or not people used validation therapy in the way Feil intended. Rather, the important thing was to try to do something therapeutic. If your preferred way of working was through cognitive therapy, then use that. If you used psychoanalytic principles, then use those. If you were a family or group therapist, well just get on and implement these. It was not as important to do a particular type of therapy, but rather that we just got on and did *something*. Use the techniques and concepts that you would normally use – and find ways of adapting these.

Almost 30 years later, I am still trying to live up to this call to action. It is one that I am sure Tom Kitwood would have agreed with – it doesn't matter what sort of psychotherapy we practice, just so long as we don't think that dementia, by definition, means that someone is *'out of psychotherapeutic reach'*.

Glossary of terms

Alzheimer's disease – this is the most common cause of dementia, typically characterized initially by changes in a person's ability to learn new verbal information and reduced verbal fluency. However, all cognitive abilities are eventually affected due to the illness's progressive nature. Currently, Alzheimer's disease can be treated, but not cured.

Assimilation of problematic experiences – this is a form of psychotherapy process research developed by the US psychologist Bill Stiles. This refers to the way in which difficult, or problematic, experiences in a person's life can be integrated into the person's self during psychotherapy. An extension of this work referred to therapy as a conversation between different internal voices – for instance between a *problematic voice*, which articulates the existence of a difficulty that needs to be faced, and a *dominant voice*, which articulates the importance of preserving the status quo.

Attachment – this refers to the enduring bonds between two people that enable each person to have a sense of security. Attachment bonds develop during a child's first few years of life and are typically thought to comprise different attachment styles. These are different behavioural styles that enable them to regulate their feelings of internal insecurity. The role of attachment behaviour as a form of emotional regulation of people living with dementia was explored by the Dutch psychologist Bère Miesen.

Carer – this describes anyone who provides care to someone living with dementia. This may refer to either a *family carer* or *caregiver* (a member of the individual's family, often providing 24-hour care and without financial recognition) or to *professional carers* (paid employees providing care in the course of their work, for instance as part of residential or domiciliary care).

Challenging behaviour – this is any behaviour that causes significant distress or danger to the person or others, or any expression of distress by the person (Bird, 2001). This may include the person shouting or crying out, behaviours such as hoarding and physical confrontations or aggression.

Cognitive dysfunction – this refers to a range of deficits associated with different causes of dementia, and includes impaired short-term memory, problem-solving, attention and the processing of visual and verbal information.

Cognitive behavioural therapy (CBT) – this is a type of talking therapy that aims to reduce emotional distress by helping people to change the way they understand and respond to situations that they find difficult.

Compassion focused therapy (CFT) – this is a form of psychotherapy that integrates techniques from cognitive behaviour therapy with concepts from evolutionary psychology. The focus of the work is to help clients to identify self-destructive patterns of behaviour, including those triggered by feelings of shame.

Containment – this is a therapeutic concept that originated in psychoanalytic therapy. In therapy it refers to the need for a therapist to tolerate the emotions being projected into them by a client without reacting punitively or by withdrawing. In dementia care it has been used to describe how family carers need to tolerate being unfairly blamed for problems that the person with dementia experiences without responding in an angry or rejecting manner.

Delirium – this refers to a deterioration in a person's cognitive functioning and includes impaired reasoning and a reduced awareness of their environment. Delirium has a physical cause (such as an infection) and has a relatively quick onset over one or two days.

Dementia – this is a condition caused by neurological impairment that is characterized by a progressive loss of neurological functioning. Dementia is caused by a variety of illnesses, including Alzheimer's disease and vascular dementia.

Dementia with Lewy bodies – people with Lewy body dementia often experience problems with alertness as well as disturbing visual hallucinations, nightmares and some of the same types of symptoms that people with Parkinson's disease experience.

Diagnostic and Statistical Manual of Mental Disorders (DSM) – the fifth edition of the DSM (DSM-5) was published in 2013 by the American Psychiatric Association and, along with the eleventh edition of the International Classification of Diseases (published by the World Health Organization) is the main taxonomic tool used by psychiatrists to make a diagnosis.

Dominant voice – this is a concept within psychotherapy process research and gestalt psychotherapy that refers to the part of the self that seeks to minimize or dismiss potential threats to self. Typically, the dominant voice articulates the need for continuity rather than change and asserts the importance of preserving an emotional status quo.

Existential threat – this refers to a threat not just to a person's health and well-being, but to the very core of a person's being or identity and their continued ability to function as a person. Typically, existential threats trigger powerful psychological responses, including denial.

Frontotemporal dementia or FTD (previously known as Pick's disease) – this is a type of dementia caused by neurological damage to the frontal and temporal lobes and is associated with cognitive changes, including a lack of empathy and difficulties in communicating. FTD can take one of three forms: behavioural-variant frontotemporal dementia (bv-FTD), primary progressive aphasia (PPA) and movement disorders.

Interpersonal psychotherapy – this is a form of psychotherapy that focuses on problems in a client's relationship with their partners, family or friends. These interpersonal challenges are thought to be associated with the development of a range of mental health symptoms, including anxiety and depression.

Living well with dementia group (LivDem) – this is an eight-session psycho-education course typically delivered within memory clinics. LivDem aims to promote adjustment to the condition by reassuring people living with dementia that they are not alone, reducing their fear of dementia and encouraging them to be more open in talking about the dementia.

Mindfulness – being 'mindful' involves paying deliberate attention to something, in the present moment and in a non-judgmental manner. The roots of mindfulness can be found in Buddhism and in Japanese Zen meditation – traditional practices that have become incorporated into a number of very different western psychotherapies.

Mnemic neglect – this is a term from social psychology that refers to the selective forgetting of information that is threatening to the self. Similar to the psychoanalytic concept of repression.

Narcissism – this refers to a personality style in which people have an inflated sense of their own self-importance, are excessively occupied with their own appearance and are uninterested in the needs of people around them. In extreme cases, this may amount to a narcissistic personality disorder.

Nostalgic memories – these tend to be about unusual events with the important people in our lives that, when they are recalled even many years later, help us to feel more connected to those people and provide a sense that our lives have been meaningful. Nostalgic memories often come from the earlier years of our lives and tend to be about things like family holidays, weddings and special times in our lives.

Person-centred counselling – this is a form of psychotherapy developed by the US psychologist, Carl Rogers in the 1940s. Therapists or counsellors offer their clients unconditional positive regard, are honest and transparent or congruent throughout the course of therapy and adopt an empathic approach to their work.

Person-centred dementia care – this is a form of dementia care created by Tom Kitwood. In person-centred dementia care, services are structured so that the needs of the individual are paramount, rather than those of the institution. Care is designed to preserve the personhood of the person with dementia, enhancing their well-being and avoiding ill-being.

Problematic voice – this is a concept within psychotherapy process research that refers to the part of the self that insists that something is wrong. In so doing the problematic voice articulates the existence of a threat to the established or dominant way that the person has habitually understood themselves and the world around them.

Projection – this refers to the process of placing one's own feelings into another person. A concept from psychoanalytic therapy, projection is often viewed as a defensive response that enables a person to articulate uncomfortable feelings without engaging with them directly.

Qualitative research – this is research in which non-numerical information that is obtained from a range of methods (such as observations, interviews or questionnaires) is analysed in order to understand the underlying concepts, experiences or opinions of participants. Qualitative research is often contrasted with quantitative research in which numerical data is collected and analysed in order to test out predictions or hypotheses.

Resilience – this is the ability to cope mentally, physically or emotionally with change, arising for instance from illness or a transition.

Respite care – this refers to the person with dementia staying for a short period, often lasting for a few days or weeks, in residential care rather than in their home. Respite care has been used within dementia care as a way of providing family carers with a break from the demands of delivering care.

Resolution therapy – this is an informal counselling approach that draws on person-centred counselling principles and was developed specifically for work with people with dementia by Graham Stokes and Fiona Goudie. Resolution therapy contends that the most appropriate response to challenging behaviour is for family and paid carers to sensitively reflect the underlying causes of a person's distress back to them, empathizing with any concealed meanings and feelings.

Self-concept – this refers to our knowledge about ourselves, who we are and the characteristics that distinguish us from other people. Self-concept develops through interactions with others, especially in our earliest years. The self-concept is related to identity, which refers to the way in which people are identified by themselves and by others.

Validation therapy – this is a type of psychotherapy developed by Naomi Feil for people living with cognitive impairments including dementia. It was the first structured form of psychotherapy to be popularized. In validation therapy, a therapist seeks to validate a person's internal withdrawal caused by a preoccupation with unfinished conflicts from earlier periods in their life.

Vascular dementia – this is a form of dementia that is caused by a reduced supply of blood to the brain resulting from damage to the network of blood vessels (the vascular system) that supply blood to the brain.

Part 1

Loss, threat and change

1 Dementia in context

The world is ageing. We are all, thankfully, living longer. According to the United Nations, in 2019 one person in eleven was aged over 65 (United Nations, 2022). However, by 2050 this figure will have risen to one in six people or 16 per cent of the world's population. In Europe and Northern America, this change is even starker – with a quarter of the population made up of older adults. These changes are most acute for what are sometimes called the '*old, old*' age group – those aged over 80 – as by 2050 the UN projects that there will be 426 million people in the world who will have achieved this milestone – a threefold increase since 2019.

While we should welcome this achievement, the increase of older people also brings with it challenges. Importantly for health and care systems, as the world ages, so also there will inevitably be an increase in those illnesses that are especially associated with ageing. Chief among these is the group of conditions which we refer to as 'dementia'. Age is the biggest risk factor for dementia. Above the age of 65, a person's risk of developing the most common forms of dementia double roughly every five years – so that while dementia affects one in fourteen people aged over 65, it affects one in six people over 80 (Alzheimer's Society, 2021). Consequently, just as the number of people aged over 65 will triple in 30 years, so too will the number of people who are living with dementia – from a global figure of around 50 million in 2018, to an anticipated 152 million in 2050. In the UK, the number of people with dementia will rise by a third between 2014 and 2025 when a million people are expected to have dementia. This rate of increase will continue so that by 2050 there will be around two million people living with dementia in the UK.

Many different illnesses cause dementia, but the majority of people who live with dementia have been affected by one of three conditions: Alzheimer's disease (which makes up roughly two-thirds of cases), vascular dementia (17 per cent), and mixed Alzheimer's and vascular dementia (10 per cent). Rarer types of dementia include Lewy body dementia (4 per cent), frontotemporal dementia (2 per cent) and Parkinson's dementia (2 per cent), with over 100 other diagnoses accounting for the remaining cases.

While dementia primarily occurs in people aged over 65, it can also affect younger people with around 42,000 living with young onset dementia (starting under the age of 65 years) in the UK – a figure that is expected to rise to over 50,000 by 2025 (Oliver et al., 2020). People with learning disabilities may be among those experiencing dementia at a relatively young age; for people with Down's syndrome, where there is a genetic link to Alzheimer's disease, the average age of onset is 55 years.

The personal and social impact of dementia

The term 'dementia' refers to the symptoms of a disease process that results from physical changes in the brain. The chief characteristic of dementia is a severe cognitive impairment that progressively extends across almost all of a person's abilities, including their memory, language and problem-solving as well as bodily functions such as movement-related difficulties and sometimes problems in swallowing. As a result of these changes, the person's ability to complete practical everyday tasks becomes progressively compromised. Answering the telephone, making a snack, getting dressed – all these comparatively simple tasks become harder and harder to complete without help. Additionally, these changes often occur at a time in life when people are also experiencing many other changes in their health and lifestyle – for instance they may be losing their hearing, needing a replacement hip or grieving the death of a partner (British Psychological Society, 2016).

Each of these different causes of dementia share three common features: while they may start with relatively discrete problems in one or two areas of cognitive functioning, eventually they come to affect almost all of the person's abilities. Although the rate at which people deteriorate varies, they are progressive in nature and for the moment at least, while treatments for different types of dementia exist, none of them address the underlying causes and consequently, none of the different forms of dementia can be cured. Moreover, as I will outline below, the main pharmacological treatments currently available for symptoms of dementia have limited benefits and are suitable for only a proportion of those diagnosed.

The different causes of dementia

The different causes of dementia are classified in the fifth and current edition of the Diagnostic and Statistical Manual of Mental Disorders (DSM-5) as major neurocognitive disorders (NCDs). Each of these conditions share the principal feature of severely impaired cognitive function and while many symptoms may overlap and be common to different illnesses, each diagnosis of dementia has its own characteristic cluster of impairments that afford unique challenges to those concerned. However, the task of differentiating the diagnosis of the different causes of dementia from one another is made more difficult, especially in the early stages, because no single test can definitively identify the presence of dementia. Instead, a number of different assessments tend to be used which, when considered together, collectively point towards a diagnosis of dementia as the most likely explanation for the problems that the person has been experiencing. Typically, therefore, diagnosing dementia is a process of excluding potential alternatives such as depression, delirium or a vitamin deficiency.

Alzheimer's disease

The onset of Alzheimer's disease is often described as insidious. It starts gradually, building up steam over time. Decline in function is progressive and, ultimately, severe. Although there are many different symptoms, these tend to begin with problems in remembering new information and a reduction in the fluency of language. As the illness progresses, so other difficulties such as with perception, coordination and initiating a sequence of behaviours begin to appear.

Vascular dementia

Vascular dementia, as the name implies, is the result of the oxygen supply to the brain being reduced due to a series of cerebrovascular accidents, or strokes, many of which occur undetected. The effects of these gradually accumulate over time resulting in cognitive problems affecting short-term memory and planning, as well as many physical challenges. The symptoms of vascular dementia, at least in the early stages, vary according to the location and extent of the lesions. Typically, vascular dementia is often diagnosed alongside other conditions, so that mixed forms of vascular dementia and Alzheimer's disease are quite common.

Other forms of dementia

Although Alzheimer's disease, vascular and mixed forms of dementia are the most common, there are also other causes of dementia. People who have been diagnosed with dementia with Lewy bodies, for instance, often experience problems with alertness as well as disturbing visual hallucinations, nightmares and some of the same types of symptoms as people with Parkinson's disease experience. Frontotemporal dementia or FTD, previously known as Pick's disease, is associated with a range of changes, including disinhibition and a lack of empathy. Where the main neurological deficit is in the temporal area of the brain, the person can also experience a significant language impairment.

The cultural and social nature of dementia

Dementia does not respect boundaries of religion, ethnicity, sex or class. Nevertheless, it is a mistake to imagine that dementia impacts on all sections of society equally. To be more precise it is important to understand that the impact of dementia does not simply depend on the extent to which a person is affected neurologically. Rather, the context in which people live will, at least in part, determine how they experience dementia, because it is this wider social context that determines what sorts of support are available, from whom and when they are likely to access this. Research consistently shows that across the world the impact of dementia differs from one community to another. For instance in the US, many Hispanic and African Americans have different experiences from many white Americans (e.g., Rivera-Hernandez et al., 2019; Hyun et al., 2020), while in Europe the same is true for many minority communities affected by dementia (Duran-Kiraç et al., 2021). In order to illustrate the way in which context affects a person's experience of dementia I will briefly outline how people from different South Asian communities (that is people whose origins are in countries such as Pakistan, India and Bangladesh) in the UK have a very different pattern of uptake of dementia services.

Of the roughly 900,000 people who are living with dementia in the UK at the present, a relatively small proportion (around 25,000 to 30,000 people) are from Black, Asian or other minority ethnic communities. However, over the next 30 years, the numbers of people from non-white British communities living with dementia will increase rapidly, by a factor of seven, compared to just a doubling in overall numbers. While the neurological impairments associated with dementia affect everyone with this syndrome regardless of ethnicity, race or gender, nevertheless these social factors shape people's experiences of dementia. For instance, people whose origins are from South Asian countries are the largest, single non-white community affected by dementia in the UK (Blakemore et al., 2018). However, South Asians living with dementia are less likely to access dementia services (All Party Parliamentary Group, 2013) or to receive evidence-based treatments, including medication for Alzheimer's disease, than are their white British counterparts (Parveen et al., 2017; Baghirathan et al., 2020). People from south Asian communities are also more likely to be diagnosed at a later stage in the illness (La Fontaine et al., 2007), when the person with dementia is often more severely impaired or in crisis (Hailstone et al., 2017). Moreover, when people from South Asian communities who are living with dementia and their family carers do receive health or social care services then this often does not meet their needs – with this client group being more likely to be cared for at home, to have a poorer quality of life and to negatively evaluate NHS dementia services (Mukadam et al., 2011; Tuerk and Sauer, 2015).

Within South Asian communities there is a greater tendency to rely on support from community groups whose staff and volunteers may lack specialist knowledge about dementia. This impacts upon care in a number of ways: firstly, South Asians with dementia are less likely to have access to specialist care and support; secondly, symptoms that are potentially treatable may be missed as they are mistakenly attributed to dementia or to ageing. The cumulative effect of these differences in service uptake means that South Asians who are living with dementia and their families may be socially and financially disadvantaged compared to their white British counterparts.

Many different reasons have been identified for these differences in service uptake – including services that are often insensitive to the needs of people from minority communities and are organized in a way that fails to recognize the profound differences between people who are affected by dementia. It is also the case that there are many cultural differences that affect how people use services including differences in how ageing and mental ill health are thought about. However, what these differences in how services are used illustrates is the important way in which while neurological impairment impacts on everyone living with dementia, the way in which it is experienced is mediated by an array of social, cultural and personal factors.

The impact of dementia

Whatever the cause of dementia, it has a profound psychological impact, affecting a person's sense of identity, how they behave, their mood, and their overall well-being, as well as all aspects of their relationships with others and their ability to manage everyday activities. Understandably, the impact of dementia is not confined to people who directly experience the condition. It also has a major effect on the individual's family and friends, their children and grandchildren. Ultimately, dementia touches almost everyone in society. Indeed, meeting the challenges created by an ageing population and by dementia have become key elements of government policy not just within the United Kingdom but across the globe, with dementia being addressed as a national priority (Rosow et al., 2011). In the UK, policy priorities have focused on achieving an early diagnosis, preventing or delaying admission into institutional care (Department of Health, 2013) and emphasizing the need to ensure that people affected by dementia can live well within the community.

Not only are the emotional costs of dementia at an individual and interpersonal level profound, but this condition also has a significant impact on the economy. Although there are various ways to try to put a figure on the economic cost of dementia, none of which are entirely accurate, one estimate is that dementia costs the UK economy £23 billion each year, and this figure is likely to rise. This greatly exceeds the costs associated with cancer, heart disease and stroke.

Can dementia be cured?

Current drug therapies for dementia focus largely on increasing the availability of a neurotransmitter called acetylcholine in the brains of people who have been diagnosed with Alzheimer's disease. Acetylcholine works within a person's brain to enable signals to be sent from one cell to another – and it is especially important in enabling different cognitive processes, such as attention and the laying down of new memories. When a brain is functioning normally, the activation of one nerve cell releases acetylcholine, which stimulates other nearby nerve cells. In order to prevent more signals being sent, an enzyme called acetylcholinesterase then breaks down the acetylcholine or metabolizes it. However, in Alzheimer's disease the amount of acetylcholine that is available in the brain is reduced.

In order to treat Alzheimer's disease, a class of drug has been developed that prevents acetylcholine from being broken down and therefore boosts levels of the neurotransmitter. These medications are known as acetylcholinesterase inhibitors, and the most commonly used of these is donepezil, which is sometimes referred to by its trade name of Aricept. However, while this type of medication can be useful for many people, especially in the early stages of Alzheimer's disease, their effectiveness is limited. Firstly, they can only be prescribed to people with Alzheimer's disease who do not have other health problems, such as a heart condition. Secondly, their impact is often relatively slight and while they can improve some aspects of a person's functioning, they are not a cure for dementia – they do not affect its underlying course. Finally, there inevitably comes the point where medication no longer produces noticeable effects. However, even though we cannot at present stop the illness, let alone reverse it, for some people using these medications and making simple lifestyle changes can slow down its progression.

While dementia can be treated, then, it cannot be cured. While scientists sometimes disagree about whether people die from dementia, or with dementia, to all practical purposes all of the different causes of dementia therefore need to be seen as terminal illnesses. Understandably, many people living with dementia and their families want to know how long they may live for – questions that are impossible to give more than a general response to. One study of almost 500 people living with Alzheimer's disease, frontotemporal dementia, vascular dementia and other forms of dementia tried to establish how long people would expect to live after they had first experienced symptoms (Loi et al., 2021). Where these had first been apparent when the person was aged under 65, then the median survival duration was just over 10.5 years. There was no difference in the length of survival between the different types of dementia. Where the age at which symptoms had become apparent was over 65, then there was a shorter survival time – with the median length being just over six years. Women from this older age group tended to live longer than did the men – as indeed is the case when people don't have dementia.

Given this brief account of the causes of dementia, a casual reader might be forgiven for imagining that there was little, if any, space for a psychological approach. Indeed, for a long time, the dominant narrative around dementia excluded the personal, the social and the historical from consideration. Rather, almost all of the things that someone living with dementia did were framed as symptoms of an underlying illness. However, if we travel back to the origins of Alzheimer's disease, then we can see that emotional and psychological factors have always been present.

The creation of Alzheimer's disease

Frau Auguste Deter was admitted to the Frankfurt Irrenschloss (or asylum) in November 1901. She was assessed by Alois Alzheimer, a relatively junior doctor at the hospital – a process which took over four days. Alzheimer asked Frau Deter a series of questions, for instance asking her to name a pencil or what she was eating. He noted that she struggled to write sentences as she forgot what she had to write and that her speech was repetitive and included words she seemed to have made up. Like many other patients at the hospital, Frau Deter seemed to have dementia. What struck Dr Alzheimer as unusual about her presentation, however, was that she was much younger than the other men and women who were admitted with similar symptoms – she was aged just 51. As would have been the norm at the early part of the twentieth century, Frau Deter never left the Irrenschloss and died there in April 1906. The cause of death was recorded as involving a number of different factors including blood poisoning and cerebral atrophy.

By the time of Frau Deter's death, her admitting doctor had left Frankfurt and was instead working at a laboratory in Munich. However, Alzheimer did not forget about the young patient with dementia-like symptoms and at his request, her brain was sent onto him for examination. In his laboratory, Alzheimer took a series of thin slices of different areas of Auguste's brain, stained these using a dye and then examined them under a microscope. In November 1906, just under five years after he had initially assessed Frau Deter, Alzheimer presented a description of her 'case' at the annual conference of German psychiatrists, combining an account of her symptoms with a description of his findings of microscopic changes to her brain. More specifically he identified two kinds of changes: the first taking place outside the nerve cells (now known as 'amyloid plaques'), the other inside ('neurofibrillary tangles').

While Alzheimer subsequently published these and similar findings, we refer to 'Alzheimer's disease' largely because of the way in which the head of the Munich laboratory, Emil Kraepelin, used these findings as part of a larger piece of work. At that time, Kraepelin was working on the eighth edition of *Psychiatrie* – a highly influential series of textbooks in which he set out the case that behaviours and experiences could be grouped together as symptoms of an illness, the causes of which were not psychological or social, but lay within the brain. The publication of this edition in 1910 contained a description of Alzheimer's findings about a case of presenile dementia – something which today we would refer to as young onset dementia. In creating 'Alzheimer's disease', so Kraepelin focused exclusively on the links between Frau Deter's hallucinations, memory lapses and confusion and the organic changes that Alzheimer had identified on the slides that he had made.

We now know a little more about Frau Auguste Deter. In 1996 her hospital notes were re-discovered, with a summary being published the following year (Maurer et al., 1997). However, there is still much that we do not know about Frau Deter – including the circumstances surrounding her admission.

Nevertheless, what is clear is that she was profoundly distressed by her dementia and by her admission. During this assessment period, Auguste was placed in an isolation room, and when she returned to her bed, she became agitated, screamed and *'showed great fear'*. She did not co-operate with the attendants and repeated over and over, *'I will not be cut; I do not cut myself'*. Alzheimer himself seemed to have been touched by her distress: when he asked her if she could remember the objects that he had shown her, she replied, *'I don't know, I don't know'* and Alzheimer sympathetically commented that *'It's difficult, isn't it?'* to which Auguste replies, *'So anxious, so anxious'*. Later, Alzheimer asked her if she was still anxious, and she replied that she was.

What makes Alzheimer's record of Auguste Deter's distress especially poignant is that we know that things did not get better for her – and that she remained in the Irrenschloss for the remainder of her life. While we can console ourselves with the thought that nobody now has to endure similar conditions, aspects of Auguste's experiences of her dementia nevertheless still resonate with the experiences of people who are living now with Alzheimer's disease. For instance, at different points in the notes Alzheimer records Auguste as saying, *'Oh God, I as good as lost myself'*, *'I have lost myself'* and *'I am lost'*.

Over 110 years later, in a memory clinic in the south-west of England, a man that I met who had recently been diagnosed with dementia described his feelings in a very similar way to Auguste Deter. He told me, *'I feel lost, I'm not in the world that I ought to be in,'* and *'I felt everything was taken away from me. The bottom has gone out of my world'*. Unlike Auguste Deter, this man was living in his home and, when I met him, it was in a modern, purpose-built clinic. Nevertheless, his description of what Alzheimer's disease was like for him echoed those of Alzheimer's first patient.

While Alzheimer's contribution to modern neuropathology is now recognized, we now also acknowledge the way in which dementia isn't simply a neurological process. It affects not just someone's brain, but their identity and security. The neurological changes have social and personal effects – and it is here that we as psychotherapists, counsellors and healthcare workers all have a role. Just as Alzheimer seems to have been able, even if in passing, to reflect compassionately with Auguste Deter about how hard the process was, and how anxious she had become, so we can continue to use these and other psychotherapy skills in our work with Alzheimer's other patients.

Final words

Dementia in all its forms presents a major public health crisis. It is also a profoundly human tragedy that affects almost a million families in the UK, and many millions more across the world. Each person affected by Alzheimer's disease and all the other causes of dementia will, like Auguste Deter over 100 years ago, have their own tale to tell. For some, their anxiety and confusion will spill out, just as it did for Alzheimer's first patient; for others, psychological and social defences may be more successful in pushing away this distress. Yet, however people respond to their dementia, it nevertheless impacts on the fundamental aspects of their self – their identity, their social relationships, their ability to create a meaningful and purposeful life and to hold onto a sense of personal continuity. In this way, dementia represents not just a threat to the person's health, but to their continued ability to function as a person. Dementia, then, represents an existential threat. In the next chapter I will go onto look at how the ways in which we protect ourselves against threats to our identity are intrinsically tied up in how we respond to dementia.

2 Managing the terror of dementia

I would like to start this chapter with a thought experiment. Imagine, for one moment, that you work for an evil genius who tasks you with developing a secret weapon with which they will blackmail the world. The villain's only conditions are that you develop an illness and that this should be utterly horrible and devastating.

You need to do some thinking. What sort of illness will you create? And when during a person's lifetime will it strike? It goes without saying that the illness you create would have to be incurable, but how precisely would it affect people? I would imagine that there is a fair chance that any illness you create would contain a number of the following ghastly elements: you might have chosen to make your illness progressive – one that starts insidiously but gradually spreads to affect all of the person's capabilities. You might have chosen an illness which will affect the most fundamental aspects of a person's being. You might consider timing the likely onset of your hideous and bespoke illness at older people who are more likely to experience other illnesses and who may also have to contend with other problems, such as the loss of eyesight or hearing.

In meeting your product brief, you will, of course, have designed something very much like Alzheimer's disease or another form of dementia. You will have produced an illness that evokes terror. An illness that everyone should be afraid of – one that poses a threat not just to our lives, but which compromises the very things that make each of us unique – our self-identity, relationships, the elements of life that provide meaning and from which we derive a sense of ourselves as someone of value and worth. In the sense that it acts as a threat not just to life, but to our very essence, dementia constitutes an existential threat.

Unsurprisingly, therefore, research confirms that most of us are frightened of developing dementia ourselves. For instance, the results of a survey carried out in 2010 by the polling group YouGov showed that 63 per cent of respondents were frightened about the prospect of growing old and having dementia, and that more people were frightened of developing dementia than they were of death (Alzheimer's Society, 2012). According to the poll, the older participants were, the more likely they were to be frightened of dementia. While the poll did not sample people who were living with dementia, it does not seem unreasonable to me to assume that had it done so, then the responses of many people who have been diagnosed with dementia would be largely similar – that they would still continue to be frightened of the condition – both in terms of what will happen to them and also about how other people will treat them.

Dementia and stigma

In considering how dementia acts as an existential threat, I will turn first to one element of this existential threat – the way that dementia acts as a social stigma, that is to say as *'an attribute, behaviour, or reputation which is socially discrediting'* and *'causes an individual to be mentally classified by others in an undesirable, rejected stereotype rather than in an accepted, normal one'* (Goffman, 1963). I will then move onto look at how people manage to live with threats without, at the same time, becoming overwhelmed with distress.

The experiences of stigma for people living with dementia

In 2012, Alzheimer's Disease International produced a landmark report on the global impact of stigma on the lives of people living with dementia (World Alzheimer Report, 2012). As part of this report, they conducted an online survey about stigma and dementia which over 2,000 people from 54 different countries completed. While most people who responded to the survey were family carers, around 5 per cent had been diagnosed with a type of dementia in the last five to six years.

Perhaps unsurprisingly, a clear majority of both respondents with dementia (over 75 per cent) and family carers (64 per cent) believed that there were negative associations, in effect a stigma, about dementia in their country. Roughly a quarter of the 127 people who were living with dementia in the English part of the survey reported that they had concealed or hidden the diagnosis of dementia from others. The most common reason that was cited for this was the social stigma attached to the diagnosis. A US participant wrote that *'In most circumstances I have found that if I have disclosed that I have dementia, my thoughts, opinions, conversations are discounted and dismissed'*. A respondent from New Zealand explained that *'I don't want people to think I'm stupid'*. One person had tried telling others, but then found that it was easier not to do so – *'I didn't [hide it] at first, thinking I could change people's idea of what a person with Alzheimer's disease was like. That we weren't all helpless. But I live alone in an apartment community now and I find in this conservative area people regard me much more positively if I don't reveal the nature of my illness. I tell those who have a real need to know'*.

In this survey participants with dementia were evenly split between those who reported that they had been, and those that said they had not been treated differently because of their diagnosis. An American respondent contrasted the response of others to her dementia with the more compassionate reactions to a cancer diagnosis: *'It's very interesting to see how people close to me act. It's almost as if they are afraid of bringing up the subject. Being a cancer survivor, I know that I was constantly asked how I was doing while I was going through treatment. With Alzheimer's, no-one asks'*. In a similar vein, a Canadian respondent living with dementia described how they were no longer consulted: '*Upon diagnosis [people think] that you have lost your intelligence and you no longer have any of the knowledge you have attained over the years. [People] no longer ask your advice on anything. [They] talk to the person you are with and not you. People can overprotect you, which robs you of your independence much quicker. It should be a gradual process that is ongoing, and care should be adjusted to the changes. People avoid conversation once you start showing you are having a word or thought retrieval problem*'. Similarly, a Canadian carer reported '*Because I knew my mother's social and former professional friends would treat her differently, I concealed the diagnosis. I wanted her to be her for as long as possible*'.

The concerns of people living with dementia about how others will see them resonate across qualitative research in the area. A Dutch study, for instance, looking at the diaries kept by 16 people living with dementia found that a person living with dementia faced all kinds of losses and was especially aware of how they had changed in '*the eyes of others*' (van Wijngaarden et al., 2019). Participants longed for a safe and accepting environment, but quite often felt scrutinized by inquisitive and disapproving looks. These changes affected and disrupted their relationships with their own body, in which they monitored themselves for change and tried to control their bodily loss of control. Feeling that they were drifting away from the important people in their lives, they longed to be taken seriously and struggled to share their internal struggle. More widely they felt increasingly disorientated when they were outside their comfort zone so instead retreated into shrinking social and physical worlds. For some, thoughts about euthanasia gave them the possibility of taking control over the dreadful future.

How does stigma affect people living with dementia?

There are two processes through which stigma impacts on dementia (Link, 1987; Link and Phelan, 2001; Link et al., 1989). The first process occurs after an individual is diagnosed with an illness such as Alzheimer's disease, if both they and the people around them assume that the ideas within their society around dementia, mental illness or ageing will apply to them. As Susan Behuniak has described, these social representations may include beliefs about people with dementia being like Zombies – neither living, nor completely dead (Behuniak, 2011). These internalized cultural stereotypes add to what is often a growing negative self-image.

The second process by which stigma can impact on a person comes from the feelings that can be triggered by having a potentially shameful attribute revealed and the strategies that a person adopts to avoid this. Western society places a strong emphasis on personal competence, independence and self-reliance – all aspects of daily life that are eroded by cognitive impairment.

People with dementia may, then, often be concerned that others will find out that they are no longer competent to make decisions, that they depend on their family for even basic aspects of self-care and that they consequently are not able to rely fully on themselves. Should what they take to be these compromised facets of their self become exposed to others, then this can engender feelings of shame – a complex pattern of painful emotions involving anger, disgust and an intense sense of self being flawed or bad with a sense of interpersonal threat of rejection or attack (Gilbert, 2009a). This is not to say, of course, that people are right to be ashamed that they have dementia or that others around them will reject or attack them. Rather, this is often how others subjectively experience their dementia.

As the British psychologist and psychotherapist Paul Gilbert has pointed out, the experience of shame is associated with behaviours aimed at the avoidance of situations where the potential shameful aspects of self-functioning may be exposed (Gilbert, 2014a). When these aspects are exposed to public view, then people may try to cover up their exposure or even to deny that the behaviour has occurred at all. These three behaviours – avoidance, cover up and denial are recurring features of the lives of many people living with dementia (Cheston, 2005). Often people living with dementia try to avoid rejection by attempting to control who knows about their dementia. For many people this involves more than just not revealing the fact that a diagnosis has taken place, but also trying to hide some of the signs of dementia – such as their memory dysfunction. This may involve avoiding situations where their cognitive deficits might be exposed, such as conversations in groups of friends. Then, should a cognitive problem be exposed, for instance if they forget the name of a good friend, they may try to cover it up by using a general term such as *'mate'*, *'pal'* or (in the case of a former client of mine, the Wiltshire slang term of *'my lover'*). Finally, if the person is directly confronted with evidence of a memory lapse, they may then entirely deny that it has occurred. Some people, especially those who have grown up within a culture that is especially prone to shame may be more likely than others to experience shame (Wong and Tsai, 2007). However, the frequent occurrence of behaviours within dementia settings that are associated with shame such as avoidance, cover up and denial suggest that stigma and shame are likely to be widely experienced by people living with dementia.

How can we reduce stigma?

Stigma prevents people from acknowledging symptoms and obtaining the help they need. It causes individuals and organizations to behave in ways that are unhelpful, emphasizing the symptoms of dementia rather than supporting the abilities that people with dementia have. However, there are ways to reduce stigma. In the UK, for instance, government policy has for the last 10 years encouraged the development of dementia-friendly communities and there are similar initiatives in many other countries. Importantly, many people living with dementia have been able to speak out and to gain platforms to inform both the general public and others living with dementia about their experiences. The DEEP Network of Dementia Voices in the UK, for instance, brings together people who are living with dementia so that they can meet for support and friendship. DEEP groups have also become involved in campaigning to raise awareness about dementia. While there is still a long way to go, we are gradually seeing the transformation of dementia into a condition about which people can speak more openly without fear of rejection. In Part 3 of this book, I will explore in more detail how we can talk to people about their dementia.

Fear of dementia and forgetfulness

Stigma, then, constitutes one aspect of the existential threat that people living with dementia are likely to experience. In order to understand how people living with dementia respond to such threats our research group has turned to the body of evidence that has accumulated over the last 30 years which suggests that, as humans, we have developed a large repertoire of strategies that buffer us against the psychological impact of threats to our self-concept (e.g., Burke et al., 2010; Pyszczynski et al., 2015). Together with my colleagues (Emily Dodd, Gary Christopher and Sanda Ismail in Bristol, and Constantine Sedikides and Tim Wildschut at the University of Southampton) I have been working over the last decade to find out whether people living with dementia are able to draw on these strategies to mitigate the impact of this threat, or whether their cognitive impairment would interfere with this protective process. While much of our research has consisted of a series of hypothesis-driven experimental studies, our findings have a clear clinical relevance: by exploring how people defend themselves against their fears about dementia, so we can better understand how to use psychological techniques, including psychotherapy, to support this adjustment.

Our starting place was to establish whether fears about the impact of dementia on the self might lead to some people apparently forgetting about their dementia. More specifically, we wondered whether people might be motivated to forget those aspects of their dementia that they experience as the most threatening. The psychological basis for this hypothesis is the Mnemic Neglect Effect or MNE (Sedikides et al., 2016). In brief, the MNE suggests that people will be better at recalling information about themselves that is positive and that relates to the central aspects of their self-concept than information that is negative (and thus more threatening). To put this another way, we have a strong tendency to selectively forget negative feedback when this relates to the core elements of our identity. We reasoned that by exploring whether people living with dementia use the MNE to mitigate the distress that they would otherwise experience as a result of knowing about their illness, we would be able to explore one of the ways in which people defend themselves against their fears of dementia.

We hypothesized that the MNE would limit the recall of people who have dementia for the most threatening aspects of the condition and have no effect on their recall of the less threatening aspects. To test this, we first generated a list of over 60 statements about dementia from self-help leaflets designed for people with dementia written either by the Alzheimer's Society or by the National Health Service. We then asked staff and students at the University of the West of England to rate these statements in terms of how threatening they were to their well-being. From their responses we selected the 12 most threatening and the 12 least threatening statements.

We then carried out a series of experiments: some with people living with dementia, and some with people who did not have dementia. The procedure for the first two studies was identical (Cheston and Christopher, 2019). We randomized the 24 dementia-related statements into four groups of six, and then read out each group to participants, recording their answers. Half of the participants had the statements read to them as if they referred directly to themselves, while the other half had them read as if they referred to a hypothetical person called Chris. One example of a highly threatening statement was, '*As the illness gets worse, so you/Chris will increasingly come to rely on others*', while a less threatening statement was, '*In the illness, proteins can gradually build-up inside your/Chris's brain*'. After being asked to recall as many of the statements as they could, participants were given a recognition task consisting of all the statements they had heard and an equal number of new statements.

In our first study we recruited 62 individuals, all of whom had a diagnosis of either Alzheimer's disease, vascular or mixed dementia. All of our participants had comparatively mild levels of dementia and had been diagnosed relatively recently, with equal numbers being randomized to remember the statements as if they referred to them, and to 'Chris'. Our results confirmed our hypothesis: the MNE meant that people with dementia recalled fewer of the most threatening dementia-related statements than they did of the least threatening ones (Cheston et al., 2018a).

In addition, when we looked at the answers that participants provided, we found that there was a consistent pattern in the mistakes that participants made when they did recall the statements. On occasion, participants reversed the emotional direction, or valence, of the statement such that it became more or less threatening. For instance, instead of recalling the highly threatening statement that the illness would make it harder to remember the name of family and friends, sometimes people would say that the illness would **not** make it harder to remember these names. At other times participants misremembered a low-threat statement, recalling it as being more severe than it actually was or repeated a sentence that they had already recalled for a second or third time. When we looked at the pattern of these intrusion errors, we found a clear difference. Compared to participants who had been instructed to think of the statements as relating to Chris, those participants who had been asked to remember statements that related to themselves were significantly more likely to reverse the high-threat statements – thereby making them less threatening – and to repeat the low-threat ones.

Taken together, our findings suggest that people living with dementia made two types of memory errors, both of which acted to protect their self from any distress caused by the most threatening statements. Firstly, our participants selectively forgot the most threatening information, but only when these related to themselves. Secondly, when our participants did make mistakes in the information that they remembered about dementia, then these mistakes again acted to protect the self against threat.

Our next study replicated this procedure but with people of all ages who did not have a diagnosis of dementia. Once again, we found that the MNE protected people against the threat to their self in the highly negative dementia statements. However, this was only the case for participants aged over 55 – the younger participants in our study did not show this effect (Cheston et al., 2020). This suggests two things: firstly, that the forgetting of dementia-related information is not just a result of cognitive impairment but is a more widespread psychological process; and secondly the most likely explanation as to why older, but not younger, people show the MNE for dementia statements is that the former group are more personally threatened by the condition.

The final way in which we have explored how selective forgetting can protect us against the threat of dementia has been to explore whether it is possible to eliminate the MNE (Green et al., 2009). The experience of being nostalgic is sometimes looked down upon, but our colleagues at the University of Southampton, Tim Wildschut and Constantine Sedikides, have, over many years, shown that nostalgic memories have a different impact compared to other types of memory – even when these are happy. Nostalgic memories tend to be about unusual events with the important people in our lives – events that when we recall them even many years later help us to feel more connected to these people and help us to feel that our lives have been meaningful (Sedikides and Wildschut, 2018; 2019). These nostalgic memories often come from the earlier years of our lives and tend to be about things like family holidays, weddings, and special times in our lives (Wildschut and Sedikides, 2020). They can be prompted by listening to music, looking at photographs, scents or visiting places (Wildschut et al., 2006). Importantly, compared to recalling an ordinary memory, recalling a nostalgic memory boosts a person's psychological resources: it increases our self-esteem, the feeling of being close to those we love and enhances our sense that life is meaningful. Nostalgic memories help us to feel that we are still the same person now as we have been in the past, and while they can be tinged with sadness (because they remind us that this part of our life is no more), the main feelings we have when we recall a nostalgic memory are positive.

A doctoral student working with me, Sanda Ismail, was able to show that people living with dementia experienced nostalgia in the same way as people without dementia (Ismail et al., 2022) and that they gained the same boost from these memories (Ismail, 2017). We therefore hypothesized that these psychological benefits might buffer the self-concept of someone living with dementia to the extent that they would be more able to be reminded about their dementia without being upset. If this was the case, then they might not need to rely on forgetting threatening information to reduce their distress. In other words, people who recalled a nostalgic memory might not need to selectively forget about dementia-related information.

In order to test this hypothesis out, we replicated our first study, but with two changes. Firstly, we randomized 50 participants with dementia to either recall a nostalgic or an ordinary memory, and secondly, we asked all of the participants to think of the statements as if they applied to them. In other words, for this study we did not use the Chris-related statements at all. The results confirmed our hypothesis: participants who remembered the nostalgic rather than an ordinary memory then went on to recall significantly more of the dementia statements about themselves, including the most threatening. Importantly, they did this without any increase in their levels of distress (Ismail et al., 2018); recalling more information had not been upsetting for them.

Managing the terror of dementia: A summary of our research findings

Our research suggests that people living with dementia use a number of strategies to protect themselves against the emotional distress that would otherwise result from knowing about their dementia. Firstly, they selectively forget the most threatening information about dementia when this applies to themselves, but not when this relates to someone else. Secondly, when they mis-remember information about dementia, then they are more likely to lower the level of threat to themselves compared to their mis-recall of statements about someone else. Finally, when we were able to boost participants' psychological resources by asking them to recall a nostalgic memory, then these participants were able to remember more of the statements about dementia, including the most threatening ones, without any increase in their levels of anxiety.

While this series of studies may seem far removed from the day-to-day lives of people living with dementia and their families, we believe that they provide important information about how people adjust to their dementia. Firstly, they show us that it is difficult for people to recall the most threatening aspects of their illness. It is easier to do so when thinking about how dementia affects other people than when this is about themselves. Secondly, if we help people to feel better about themselves, then they can remember more information. In other words, remembering information about dementia relates to threat – if we make information less threatening or we boost the person's self-concept, then people will remember more. These are themes that I will return to later in this book when I discuss how psychotherapists can help people to adjust to their dementia.

Final words

As a clinical psychologist working in a memory clinic, I had many different roles. Sometimes I was responsible for carrying out or supervising the assessment of the level of cognitive functioning of patients as part of the diagnostic process. At other times, I provided a psychotherapeutic role – allowing space for individuals and couples to talk about how dementia was affecting their lives. When I talked to my colleagues, doctors, nurses and other psychologists, I was sometimes struck by how often they seemed to either forget about or to underestimate the psychological impact of dementia on the people they were assessing. Sometimes I too was guilty of this. The people we worked with were good at putting on a brave face when we met them – often reacting stoically and in an understated way to the diagnosis. Perhaps some had been half expecting it. Perhaps it was just part of a phlegmatic, cultural response – the sort of coping mechanism that can sometimes be dismissed as putting a brave face on the situation.

However, when we dig deeper, then it becomes clear that dementia has the potential to be profoundly upsetting. As I spent time talking to my clients and exploring their experiences of dementia, so many of the people that I worked with in my clinic talked about their fears of dementia and their concern as to how the condition would diminish or reduce them as human beings. They were painfully aware that regardless of the specific type of dementia that they had been diagnosed with, it had the capacity to take away some of the most precious aspects of their being. They wondered whether, in reducing their capacity to remember the names of their own children or to recognize their husband, wife or partner, dementia might make them less of a partner. Many, too, were profoundly distressed that the important 'others' in their life might think less of them and that they might even be admitted against their will to a psychiatric hospital or care home. In other words, they were all too aware of the social stigma that their diagnosis carried.

It is precisely because dementia carries with it this layered threat of diminishment and abandonment that I believe it is appropriate to describe it as an existential threat. Dementia is not just a potential threat to health and wellbeing, but something that also compromises the very core of a person's being. All too often society tends to deal with this existential threat by avoiding a discussion of the human consequences of dementia, for instance by holding onto beliefs that people living with dementia are unaware of what is happening to them. Often this social resistance to thinking and talking about dementia limits the opportunities available for people to talk about their experiences of living with the disease. In the next chapter I will go on to look at why it is important that we provide these opportunities to talk about the impact of dementia.

3 | We need to talk about dementia

Until the start of the Covid-19 pandemic in the spring of 2020, I worked for seven years at the memory clinic run by RICE (or the Research Centre for the Care of Older people) in Bath, a city in the South West of England. The memory clinic's main function was to assess people who had concerns about their cognitive functioning, and to determine whether they met the diagnostic criteria for one of the many different types of dementia. My role was to provide a psychotherapy clinic each week to people who had been assessed and diagnosed as having an illness such as Alzheimer's disease. Typically, I would offer people time to talk over with me how their dementia was impacting their lives. Often, I would meet couples – where one of the partners in the couple had been diagnosed with a form of dementia – and encourage them to talk to each other about their thoughts, their fears and their hopes. Appointments lasted for fifty minutes and occurred once a month or sometimes once every three months. I have included anonymized descriptions of some of this work in this book.

On occasion I met people who, from the start of our work, talked openly about their dementia and reflected poignantly on the most upsetting aspects of their condition. However, more often, the people I met found it hard to talk about their illness, either forgetting important details or being greatly distressed when they recalled them. Sometimes my clients might forget that they had been told about their diagnosis, or they might insist that they could still do everything they had always done even when being contradicted by their partner. These memory lapses seemed to me to be very similar to the recall errors I have described in Chapter 2 and I tended to think that they functioned in the same way by protecting the people in the clinic against the threat of dementia. As our work progressed, however, most of my clients would begin to feel safe enough to explore their illness with me – and as they did so, they became more able to talk about what was happening to them and more at ease with themselves.

There were many different reasons why individuals and couples found it hard to talk openly about dementia. For some, the reasons paralleled the evidence my colleagues and I had gathered in our 'laboratory-based' experiments around the MNE that I described in the last chapter. For these clients, the thought of progressively deteriorating over time, losing aspects of themselves that were so precious to them was devastating. For others, it was their fear about what others (often including their partners) would think about them. In these cases, it was the social stigma that surrounds dementia that made it hard for people to address the changes that they were experiencing.

The process of talking about dementia is, however, not straightforward. Often it is a conversation that healthcare professionals either routinely avoid or simply do not see as part of their remit or within their skill set. In this chapter I will argue that while we should not assume that people want to talk about their dementia or that doing so will always be helpful, nevertheless I believe that for many people who have dementia it is important to have an opportunity to talk about what is happening.

Should healthcare professionals talk about dementia?

I have been fortunate over the course of my career that the majority of doctors I worked alongside found compassionate ways to disclose a diagnosis of dementia to their patients and their families. However, this is not always the case. Indeed, until relatively recently, many clinicians were reluctant either to give the diagnosis or even in some cases to make a diagnosis at all. Thankfully this silence around diagnosing dementia is much rarer now. However, even today, many healthcare professionals are often reluctant to have a conversation with the people they work with about their dementia, out of a concern that this will be too upsetting. While I recognize that not everybody who has dementia either wants to talk about it or would benefit from doing so (topics I will return to later in this chapter and in Part 4), many others will benefit from these discussions. If we, as healthcare professionals, can't talk about dementia with the people that we diagnose then there is a risk that we will be collectively entering into a conspiracy of silence about dementia. One of the facilitators in a LivDem group (see Chapter 6) fed back to me about a conversation she had with her supervisor, who suggested to her that '*if the professionals can't say the word dementia, well how are they [her clients living with dementia] going to accept their diagnosis and move forward? And that really, you know, made sense to me. You know, really made me think, "Oh my word, I've never thought of it like that"*'.

The skills most associated with having these sorts of open conversations are sometimes referred to as 'active listening skills'. They include the listener paying attention to what they are being told, showing that they are listening and responding appropriately in a non-judgemental way. Good listening skills are integral components for all forms of talking therapies, from person-centred counselling to cognitive behaviour therapy and other forms of psychotherapy (issues that I will return to in later sections of this book). Talking to someone who is a 'good listener' helps us to feel that we are being taken seriously and encourages us to explore and understand problems that we may be facing. At the same time, active listening does not just take place within psychotherapy or counselling sessions – many people use these skills instinctively as part of encounters in their everyday life. However, for some people, active listening skills need to be practiced and developed.

Perhaps surprisingly, many healthcare professionals do not routinely learn active listening or counselling skills during training. However, when they are taught, and clinicians feel more confident in using them, then the results can be surprising. In one study, community psychiatric nurses (CPNs) were taught to use counselling skills in their work with people who had dementia (Weaks et al., 2009). As a result, their clients felt listened to and treated as a person, while the nurses developed skills themselves that they were able to use elsewhere in their professional lives. This study showed that CPNs potentially had an important role in offering emotional and practical support to people with dementia and their families who have been recently diagnosed with the counselling skills enabling the CPNs to address the psychosocial needs arising from their diagnosis more effectively.

Do people living with dementia want to know about their diagnosis?

In a UK study of 50 people with mild levels of impairment caused by their dementia and their family carers, all but one of the participants said that they would want to know if they were diagnosed with cancer – with only slightly fewer (92 per cent) also wanting to be informed about their diagnosis of dementia (Pinner and Bouman, 2003). Similar levels of carers said that they would want to be told if they were to develop either dementia or cancer. More recent research paints a similar picture – namely that the vast majority of people with probable dementia want to be informed about their diagnosis (Robinson et al., 2011). At the same time studies also consistently suggest that some people (in some cases as many as one third of people interviewed) do not want to know what is wrong, and that their wishes also need to be respected (Marzanski, 2000). Nevertheless, over the years a shift has taken place, so that nowadays, in the UK at least, the default position tends to be that a person with probable dementia has the right to know about their diagnosis, should they wish to do so, and that for many knowing about their dementia may also be empowering (Bamford et al., 2004; Bortolotti and Widdows, 2011).

How do people react to being told their diagnosis?

Studies consistently show that people with dementia experience a wide range of emotions on receiving their diagnosis and that they react to the disclosure in different ways. While some people are shocked and react with disbelief and anger (Byszewski et al., 2007), others say that it had confirmed their suspicions (Derksen et al., 2006) and that they are relieved that their symptoms have an

explanation (Pratt and Wilkinson, 2003). For many people their most immediate worries after receiving a diagnosis relate to a fear of the unknown and an
unfolding sense of loss. In particular, the social stigma of receiving a diagnosis
of dementia is often a key issue (Husband, 2000), with many people being concerned that others will find out and that they may be socially embarrassed by
their poor memory or another type of cognitive failure. Consequently, as I
described in the last chapter, some people with dementia are hyper-vigilant,
watching for evidence of a memory slip, and when these occur then attempting
to 'cover up' or minimize their difficulties (Bahro et al., 1995; Husband, 2000).

Two research studies shed some light on whether, in retrospect, people
believe that receiving the diagnosis had been helpful to them – while both of
these studies took place over 20 years ago, nevertheless their results are still
likely to be relevant now. Bachman et al., (2000) interviewed 35 consecutive
referrals to a memory clinic between three and twelve months after they had
been given a diagnosis of Alzheimer's disease. Over two thirds (69 per cent) of
family carers thought it was a good idea to tell the patient the diagnosis, with
almost three quarters (74 per cent) saying that it had not been too upsetting.
Even where the person with dementia was judged to have been 'very upset',
their carers still thought that the honest discussion of the diagnosis had been
helpful. The second study (Smith et al., 1998) produced very similar results with
almost all family carers reporting that they found it helpful both for themselves
(98 per cent) and for their relative (84 per cent). These two studies, then, suggest that although there may be short-term distress, most carers report that
receiving the diagnosis had been helpful. Indeed, a review of the literature carried out 10 years ago concluded similarly that although there may be short-term
distress, the majority of people with dementia did not experience long-
term negative effects after receiving their diagnosis (Robinson et al., 2011).

What impact does knowing about a diagnosis have?

One area of post-diagnostic adaptation to the diagnosis of dementia that has
been studied in some depth relates to whether people who seem to be more
aware of their diagnosis have worse outcomes in terms of a poorer quality of
life, or a higher presence of psychiatric symptoms. The results of these studies
paint a rather confused picture. Thus, some studies do show a relationship
between low levels of awareness about a diagnosis and poorer outcome, such
as challenging behaviour and higher levels of family caregiver burden (Clare
et al., 2004). At the same time, there is also evidence that higher levels of
awareness may also be problematic and aggravate changes in mood including
depression and anxiety (Aalten et al., 2005; 2006).

One of the largest and best funded studies to explore this area is the Improving the experience of Dementia and Enhancing Active Life, or IDEAL, study in
the UK. Alexander et al. (2021) reported the relationship between awareness
and self-reported quality of life, well-being and life satisfaction ('living well'),
and caregiver stress using cross-sectional data from over 900 people with

mild-to-moderate levels of dementia and family carers. Of the people that they interviewed, 83 were classified as having 'low awareness', 731 people with 'some awareness', and 103 people with a 'high awareness' of their condition and diagnosis. Their results showed that psychosocial factors such as lower levels of mood, optimism and self-esteem were stronger predictors of awareness than were cognitive and functional ability. People with higher levels of awareness reported lower levels of mood and scored less well on measures of living well, optimism and self-esteem.

Awareness is, however, a deceptively tricky area to study as it presents a number of methodological challenges. Some of the challenges of carrying out this type of research can be illustrated by a series of conversations that I had with a couple in my clinic who I will call Anna and Philip. I had known and worked with this couple for several years (Cheston, 2021). In all of that time Anna refused to acknowledge her diagnosis of Alzheimer's disease. She was a complex woman, who was capable of being charming and engaging, yet also angry and dismissive of her husband whenever he challenged her. Throughout my work with them, Anna maintained that she had not changed at all – that she was just the same person as she had always been, and that while her body may have slowed down, she still did all of the things that she valued, such as sewing, seeing friends and relatives. Whenever she lost or forgot anything then she either refused to accept that this had happened, or blamed her husband, at first in a semi-humorous way, and then more forcefully. Philip, for his part, struck me as a patient, caring and sympathetic man who was constantly on the look-out to avoid situations that Anna would find challenging and willing, for the most part, to contain the anger that his wife directed at him without responding in a way that provoked her further.

My impression, from all that they told me over the years, was that Anna displayed many features of narcissism – an area that I will explore in more depth in Chapter 12. In essence, people with narcissistic traits have a fragile sense of identity that they protect by maintaining a high level of external self-esteem. Anna needed to maintain the illusion that she was unchanged because to admit to even a simple failing would have been overwhelming for her. Consequently, everything in her life was devoted to maintaining the illusion that she was unaffected and unchanged.

Patients at RICE were often offered the opportunity to take part in large research studies, and Philip and Anna took part in the study reported by Alexander and her colleagues. During one of my sessions with them, while Anna was in the toilet, Philip wistfully described to me their recent participation in this study which he felt encapsulated something of his relationship with Anna. He recounted how Anna had told the researcher that her life was wonderful – that she was still busy and active and could do all the things that she wanted to. He knew that what she had told them wasn't true, but they didn't seem particularly interested in what he had to tell them. From my knowledge of Anna, I think it is highly likely that she would have both been placed in the low awareness category, and yet also scored at a high level for self-reported quality of life. Yet, in reality, Anna's life was circumscribed and limited. She was in some regards an unreliable narrator on both her dementia and her life. Her narcissistic traits meant that she needed to maintain a position in which nothing had changed in her life – neither her cognitive abilities, nor her social life. By contrast, many of the people that I met at RICE who were able to talk meaningfully about their dementia would have been more cautious in their assessment of their quality of life.

Adjusting to dementia – responding to fear and loss

The evidence, then, suggests that most people want to be told about their dementia and that, although painful at first, this disclosure generally does not lead to serious, long-term reactions. However, all too often, once people have been told their diagnosis, there are few opportunities for them to continue to discuss its impact on their life. Disclosure becomes a one-off event, rather than a process of discussion. The important people in their life – their family and partner – may not know how to go about talking about the dementia and may avoid doing so because they know talking about it may be upsetting. All too often, health and social care professionals are either not available or avoid talking about the dementia. However, without opportunities to discuss the dementia people have a reduced chance to adjust to what is happening – in effect after being initially raised, the subject of dementia subsequently becomes something of a taboo.

The consequences of this silence about dementia are that the emotions associated with it, including peoples' fears about it, are often not addressed. In the absence of a place to talk about and to work through their distress, so the person with dementia may be more likely to avoid situations in which their difficulties are exposed. One recent study supports the possibility that fears about memory dysfunction led to both a lower quality of life and also to more actual memory failures among older people (Farina et al., 2020). The researchers asked 67 people aged between 59 and 81 to complete a self-report scale designed to capture different aspects of their fear of memory loss. They also asked participants to complete scales to assess their perceived memory failures, their quality of life, scales to assess their mood and an objective measure of memory performance. After adjusting their results to take into account the person's objective memory performance and their anxiety levels, they found that the more frightened the participants were about their memory lapses, the more they avoided situations because of this, then the lower their quality of life was, and the more likely they were to perceive themselves as having a poor memory. The authors suggested that the best way to make sense of these findings was that people who are frightened by their memory lapses begin to withdraw from activities as a way of coping with these failures and that, over time, this combination of fear and avoidance begins to impact negatively on their everyday functioning.

While the study by Francesca Farina and her colleagues was with older people without dementia, my clinical experience is of similar processes occurring among people who have dementia in which fear and avoidance lead to a worse quality of life. More specifically, the dysfunctional patterns of fear and avoidance that Farina's study identified are processes that can potentially be prevented and treated through psychological interventions, including psycho-education and psychotherapy (Fratiglioni et al., 2020).

Any process of adjustment, then, must focus on the emotional responses that people have to their dementia, including their fear, guilt and distress. In order to glimpse something of what this process might involve, we need to take an empathic leap and to think back into our own lives about the powerful emotions that even a minor, temporary lapse of memory can set off.

Adjusting to dementia

I am extremely grateful, that for now at least, I do not have a personal or immediate knowledge of the challenges of adjusting to dementia. Consequently, I have to imagine something of what must be involved.

One way to enter this imaginary space for me is to remember a recent occasion when I became angry and frustrated with myself. Early one evening I had been working on my laptop and at the same time using my phone to pay for online shopping. At the point when I prepared to go to bed, I realized that I couldn't find my wallet and mobile phone. As I hunted for them, I became progressively more and more frustrated that I couldn't find them, searching high and low. I wanted to go to bed but I couldn't do so because I needed to find my wallet and phone for the train journey to work the next day. In desperation I tried using another phone to call my mobile, hoping that I would hear it ring, but even this didn't work.

My family kindly tried to help me, but I snapped back at them, which also made me feel guilty as I had only recently told my son off for behaving just like this. I was aware that I should be coping better and was annoyed at myself for not taking more care with my possessions but thinking about this made things worse.

Finally, success! I realized that I absent-mindedly put the phone and wallet away with my laptop. I thought what an idiot I had been not to have looked there earlier. I became aware that the upset of not knowing where my phone and wallet were, and the inconvenience of looking for them had been multiplied by anger, guilt and shame – all of which make me use inefficient search strategies.

Episodes like this, are, I suspect, common to many people. While they may provide only a partial analogy of the experiences of people with dementia, they point to how difficult it must be for people to adjust to these changes. Just this one, simple, mundane episode of forgetfulness generated frustration leading to conflict and distress intensified by feelings of guilt (at being upset) and shame (at having this flaw in my personality).

Even worse, this may bring up thoughts about the future – that if this is the start of an illness, then things may get even worse. Often the people I have spoken with in my clinic told me that they found it too hard to go to this place in their minds, and consequently they tended to shut off thinking about that part of themselves and their life. For them the temptation was to try and pretend that there was nothing wrong.

Final words

Looking back at my clinical work, my impression is that the people that I met who seemed to have adjusted to their dementia most effectively recognized both that while so much about them had changed there was much that had stayed the same; they saw themselves as being both the same person but also as being different.

If we are to help people to adjust to their dementia – to be the same but different – then we need to be able to enable them to find words that help to shape or form their internal world. This can be easier to achieve if we provide people with dementia with opportunities to meet others who share their diagnosis, so that they can listen to their experiences, share their own accounts without fear of being judged and learn that they are not alone. It can be easier for people with dementia to work their way through their guilt about the burden they fear they place on others if they can discuss this with someone they love. It can be easier for a client to forgive themselves for the things that they forget or can no longer do if they talk with a skilled therapist who helps them to feel compassion for themselves. These are all opportunities that can be available through psychotherapy – be this individual work, couples counselling or group therapy. It is to this subject of how psychotherapy in its different modalities can make a difference to the lives of people living with dementia that I will now turn.

Summary of Part 1: Loss, threat and change

Dementia is a profoundly human tragedy that affects almost a million families in the UK, and many more across the world. In whatever way people respond to their dementia, it impacts on the most fundamental aspects of their being – it is an existential threat. Consequently, thinking about dementia can be profoundly upsetting – even if many people try to *'put a brave face on'*. For those around the person who has dementia, whether this is their family or paid carers, then it can be tempting to go along with this. The danger, however, it that what emerges is an unspoken agreement not to talk about the dementia. For some people, the level and type of neurological change does indeed mean that it becomes almost impossible for them to think about their dementia, but for the majority of people at least some level of awareness is possible. At the same time a social resistance to thinking and talking about dementia can have the effect of limiting the opportunities available for people to talk about their experiences of living with dementia. This in turn is likely to make it harder for many people living with dementia to adjust to their condition.

Implications for people living with dementia

Everyone with dementia will respond to what is happening differently. There is no single, 'best' way of coping – each person living with dementia will find their own way through this condition. Many people living with dementia should think about the following points.

- They may well have questions about what is going to happen or need time and space to sort things out for themselves, or they may just want to be left alone and to get on with their life. However, if there are opportunities to talk to people about their illness, then they may find this helps. A problem shared is (sometimes) a problem halved.
- They may find it helpful to remember that dementia affects many people. There is much more awareness about dementia now, partly because of the many people who have been open about their illness. This has helped to change attitudes, and they may be surprised how accepting people are now. If there are opportunities to meet others who have been diagnosed with dementia, then this may help someone living with dementia to feel less on their own.

- Many people living with dementia have a good quality of life and live well. It is possible to adjust to the condition, even if they are overwhelmed at first.
- While there will be much about the person that changes, there will be more that stays the same.

Implications for family carers

People who are caring for someone with dementia should think about the following points.

- They should look after themselves. They will have their own sense of loss and change to make sense of.
- If there are opportunities to do so, then the person they are caring for may find it helpful to occasionally acknowledge that life has changed. This doesn't need to be a long conversation, but gently acknowledging how the situation has changed can help couples, families and friends to be closer to each other.
- It can be easier for people with dementia to work their way through their feelings about what is happening if they find a space to discuss this. For some, this is best done within their family or with friends. For others, talking is easier with a counsellor or therapist – either as an individual or as a couple.

Implications for therapists

Healthcare professionals whose jobs involve offering specific counselling or psychotherapy sessions should think about the following points.

- They should not be afraid or reluctant to offer psychotherapy sessions to people living with dementia.
- They should be aware that dementia represents a major public health challenge. For many people living with dementia, as well as their family carers, psychotherapy provides an important way to make sense of what is happening and to adjust to the changes that it brings.

Implications for professionals and workers in dementia care

Staff working in dementia care should think about the following points.

- They should not underestimate the psychological impact of dementia on the people they work with. People are good at putting on a brave face when we met them. Often, the staff working with them need to go along with this – but there may be opportunities to be curious about how things *really* are.

- They should ensure that they feel confident using active listening skills – including receiving training in this. Staff teams need to be open in recognizing that having a space in their service to allow people to discuss how dementia is affecting them is important.

- They should listen out for instances where people acknowledge that their life has changed. The core skills of dementia care include active listening – paying attention to what people say and showing that you're listening and interested in what they have to say. If staff feel confident enough and have received training, then they can also consider using basic counselling skills to facilitate discussion.

- When a team member talks to someone about any aspects of their dementia, including disclosing the diagnosis, then they should record this in the person's notes. This includes recording what has been told, by whom, where and how. Other members of the team who then read the notes will know what has been discussed, which will facilitate future conversations.

Part 2

Psychotherapy in practice

4 Individual psychotherapy

The ability of psychotherapy to help people to resolve emotional threats, to take greater control over their lives and in some cases to adjust to life's challenges means that psychotherapy has much to offer people living with dementia. There are, however, many challenges in using psychotherapy for those affected by dementia: not only is there the impact of the neurological impairment, but the emotional weight of a diagnosis and the residual social difficulties in talking about dementia can all make it difficult for clinicians to find ways to engage meaningfully with people affected by dementia.

Over 20 years ago, I carried out a narrative review of how psychotherapy was being used in dementia care (Cheston, 1998). While I was able to identify examples from all of the main models of psychotherapy, most research involved qualitative analysis or case studies. Although these papers illustrated the potential for psychotherapy and described, for instance, how therapy could be adapted or the types of change that were possible, only a handful of studies had collected hard evidence about the impact of this work – too few to be able to come to any conclusions.

Almost 20 years later, I returned to this area together with Ada Ivanecka and published a second review. This time we found 26 studies, all of which had used the sorts of methodology that were likely to produce more definitive evidence. Since then, two further reviews have appeared – both of which included a slightly different range of studies, for instance including psychotherapy with family carers. Shoesmith et al. (2020) looked at 31 papers, of which 4 were solely for the person with dementia, 15 for family caregivers and 12 delivered to both the person with dementia and their caregivers. Sukhawathanakul et al. (2021) identified 24 papers that examined the effects of psychotherapeutic interventions on outcomes related to acceptance and adjustment, of which 15 studies examined interventions targeted towards individuals with cognitive impairment, with the remaining nine studies also targeting their caregivers.

One of the striking things about each of these reviews was how widespread the reports of psychotherapy were. While many studies used the more directive forms of psychotherapy, such as cognitive behavioural and problem-solving therapy, there were also studies of more exploratory work – such as interpersonal and psychodynamic therapy. Therapy was delivered through individual, couples and group formats with studies coming from a wide range of countries including Germany, Italy, Denmark and Norway as well as from Japan, the US and the UK. All of the studies, however, described adapting the therapeutic intervention to meet the changing needs of clients – and all of them, even those reporting individual psychotherapy with the person living with dementia, made sure to involve a family caregiver in the therapeutic process.

Yet, despite this upsurge of interest, there is still a need for more research in this area. Some studies are poorly designed or reported, while many others are relatively small, often with thirty people in each of the intervention and control arms of the study – too few for us to be able to draw meaningful conclusions. While the strongest evidence for the usefulness of psychotherapy is for work directed at family caregivers, nevertheless there is also good evidence of therapy being effective for people living with dementia – especially for group interventions that were provided relatively soon after a diagnosis had been made.

In this chapter, I will provide an overview of some of this work and try to give a flavour of its richness and heterogeneity. There are many different ways to define psychotherapy, but in this book I will use the term to describe a process that occurs in an interpersonal context, on a regular basis with the aim of helping a person to change their way of being in the world, their behaviour or otherwise to enhance their well-being. Psychotherapy achieves this by enhancing a person's understanding of their lives, their relationships and recurring patterns of thinking and behaving. I will focus on forms of psychotherapy that are primarily verbal in nature and consequently, I will not be looking at therapies that do not focus primarily on talking (such as art and music therapy) nor those psychological interventions that do not explicitly aim to change a person's feelings, thinking or behaviour (such as cognitive stimulation therapy or reminiscence therapy).

I will also focus on four, broad therapeutic domains: cognitive behavioural therapy, person-centred counselling, psychodynamic psychotherapy and interpersonal therapy. However, as I have indicated above, the research literature has expanded greatly in recent years; there is now an extremely wide range of qualitative descriptions and case reports. In principle, at least, there is unlikely therefore to be an obstacle to working with a person living with dementia within any therapeutic perspective, especially if they are in the earliest stages of the condition.

Cognitive behavioural therapy

Cognitive behavioural therapy or CBT refers to a very broad range of talking therapies, which are linked by a shared concern to focus on the way in which recurring patterns of thoughts and behaviours impact on a person's feelings. In the UK context, CBT of different forms is widely used – and it is therefore perhaps unsurprising that there have been many reports of CBT being used within dementia care. In this brief review I will focus on three forms of CBT: firstly a focus on depression and anxiety similar in many ways to that created by Aaron T. Beck (e.g., Beck, 1997) and then two variations on this – mindfulness-based cognitive therapy, and compassion-focused therapy.

CBT for depression and anxiety

One of the first reports of CBT being used with people living with dementia was provided by the US psychologists Linda Teri and Dolores Gallagher-Thompson (Teri and Gallagher-Thompson, 1991). They described how, over an average of 16 to 20 sessions, patients were encouraged to identify and then to challenge their cognitive distortions, generating more adaptive ways of viewing specific situations and events.

More recently, a series of UK studies have also had encouraging results. A relatively small study of cognitive therapy with seven clients with dementia and depression found modest, but statistically significant changes in depression as a result of the intervention (Scholey and Woods, 2003). In a slightly larger pilot study, Aimee Spector and her colleagues used a 10-session person-centred form of CBT with people with mild to moderate cognitive impairments and clinically significant levels of anxiety, working with the person with dementia and their caregiver together (Spector et al., 2015). Their aim was to reduce symptoms of anxiety by increasing a sense of safety and self-efficacy. However, while they found a significant fall in depression, the improvement in anxiety was non-significant after adjusting for pre-intervention differences. As is often the case within research trials, their intervention was delivered by experienced staff (in this case four clinical psychologists) and consequently the results may be harder to replicate with less experienced practitioners.

Probably the most well-researched form of CBT with people living with dementia is the Problem Adaptation Therapy or PATH Study (Kiosses et al., 2010, 2011 and 2015). PATH aimed to support people living with dementia and their family carers to use tools such as calendars and notebooks to find a way around the behavioural and functional problems caused by their cognitive impairment and thus to reduce depression. PATH was found to be effective in reducing depression and disability at 12 weeks for depressed participants with varying degrees of cognitive impairment. This series of studies was well designed, meaning that we can have a high degree of confidence that PATH is beneficial for people with dementia.

Using cognitive behavioural therapy in conjunction with other interventions

An important aspect of CBT is its flexibility – for instance it can readily be combined with other types of intervention. One example of this is the CORDIAL Study (Kurz et al., 2012) which incorporated behavioural strategies such as activity planning and daily structuring into a multi-modal intervention for people with mild levels of cognitive impairment caused by Alzheimer's disease. Although levels of daily functioning were unchanged, quality of life and depression levels improved for a group of female participants. Similarly, Stanley et al.

(2013) used a modified form of CBT that incorporated religious elements and a simplified package of training in skills such as breathing, calming thoughts and sleep hygiene. They described this as '*the Peaceful Mind*' intervention and reported significant improvement in levels of anxiety and quality of life for participants with mild and moderate levels of dementia. A third adaptation of CBT combined bi-weekly therapy with tai chi exercises and attendance at a support group over a 40-week period for people in the early and mid-stages of dementia (Burgener et al., 2008). This found limited improvement in participants' cognitive functioning and self-esteem.

Mindfulness-based cognitive therapy

Being 'mindful' involves paying attention on purpose, in the present moment, and in a non-judgemental manner (Kabat-Zinn, 2013). The roots of mindfulness can be found in Buddhism, as well as Japanese Zen meditation – traditional practices that have become incorporated into a number of very different western psychotherapies. These include two techniques that are sometimes described as part of a 'third wave' of cognitive behavioural therapies. The first of these is, mindfulness-based stress reduction or MBSR which typically involves eight weekly group sessions with daily, 45-minute home practice (Grossman et al., 2004). Secondly, mindfulness-based cognitive therapy or MBCT combines meditation techniques and elements of cognitive behavioural therapy (Segal et al., 2018). Both techniques aim to develop participants' aware-ness of their relationship to their thoughts and feelings and to teach specific skills around managing distress, especially around anxiety and stress.

Mindfulness is increasingly being used with people with cognitive impair-ments including those living with dementia. As for other forms of CBT, sessions are adapted to meet the needs of participants – most commonly by reducing the duration of sessions and using memory aids. Therapist behaviour also changes, including using simplified language and repeating material more often (Chan et al., 2020).

Chan et al. (2017) report data from the Mindfulness Program, a 10-session twice weekly intervention delivered in residential care. Within sessions there is a mindful warm-up activity in which each participant takes turns to hold a soft ball and spends a brief moment to pause, think, and share with the group how they feel at that moment; this is then followed by two guided mindfulness meditations (mindful breathing and either mindful movement or a body scan – a form of mindfulness meditation where the person deliberately pays atten-tion to the feelings of each part of their body in turn, checking for anything out of the ordinary). After each guided meditation the group then discusses the activity to help participants explore their thoughts, feelings, and sensations, including any pain they are experiencing. The Mindfulness Program requires facilitators to have their own mindfulness practice in order for them to be able to embody the core attitudes of mindfulness practice: a non-judgemental approach, patience, trust, non-striving, acceptance and letting go (Kabat-Zinn,

2013). Adapting a mindful stance in this way also means that facilitators do not strive for a particular result from participants; it enables them to adopt a curious approach that embraces uncertainty. Between sessions, participants are encouraged to practice mindful breathing and meditation – and in order to support this, staff members are actively encouraged to attend the group whenever possible.

In this study, 20 participants with mild to moderate dementia were randomly allocated to attend the Mindfulness Program compared to 11 who received usual care. Those in the Mindfulness Program made significant improvements in quality of life compared to those in the control condition, although there were no changes in levels of mood, cognitive functioning or stress (Churcher Clarke et al., 2017). Qualitative analysis of interviews carried out with a combination of participants, family carers and course facilitators identified several beneficial effects. These included participants being able to share their experiences, a greater focus on the present and positive emotional changes, such as increased self-compassion (Douglas et al., 2021).

A larger, two-year study compared 120 people diagnosed with Alzheimer's disease who were randomly allocated to receive three sessions each week of either mindfulness, cognitive stimulation therapy or relaxation (Quintana-Hernandez et al., 2016). At the end of this period, people in the mindfulness arm of the study scored at a significantly higher level of cognitive functioning than did those in the control or relaxation conditions. Given the longitudinal nature of this study, the authors suggested that their findings provided good evidence that mindfulness could be used as a non-pharmacological treatment to slow cognitive impairment for people with Alzheimer's disease.

Compassion focused therapy

Compassion focused therapy (CFT) has grown out of the work of a British psychologist and psychotherapist, Paul Gilbert (Gilbert, 2009b). Gilbert sets out how humans evolved as social creatures with a range of cognitive competencies for reasoning, reflection, anticipating, imagining and creating a socially contextualized sense of self (Gilbert, 2014b). However, the need for a social brain, in which people can imagine a version of themselves as others see them has caused conflicts to arise, so that we can become easily triggered into destructive behaviours and mental health problems. One of these 'tricky brain' procedures occurs when people experience shame – a form of self-criticism in which the person comes to see themselves as possessing a fundamental flaw which they cannot tolerate being revealed to others (Gilbert and Woodyatt, 2017). As I argued in Part 1 of this book where I outlined the impact of stigma, shame is often an enduring presence in the lives of many people living with dementia (Holst and Hallberg, 2003; Cheston, 2005; Aldridge et al., 2019).

Gilbert has suggested that where these tricky brain states, including shame, exist, it is important to give people the psychological resources that they need to forgive themselves. Key to this is to build self-compassion. Within this context, CFT may have an important role to play in working with people living with dementia – and indeed one of the series editors for this book, Keith Oliver, who was diagnosed with early onset Alzheimer's disease at the age of 55, has described how the idea of writing a book about his own experiences of Alzheimer's disease came from receiving CFT (Oliver, 2019).

Despite the potential of compassion-focused work to address the impact of shame arising from stigma, to date I have only come across one example of a systematic research programme using CFT with people living with dementia (Craig et al., 2018; Collins et al., 2018). This involved a case series of work with seven clients in order to assess the feasibility of using CFT. Over the course of the intervention, the study found improvements in mood, anxiety and self-compassion with three participants moving out of the clinical depression range. However, given the relatively small-scale nature of the study, further work is clearly required before we can draw any conclusions about its effectiveness.

Counselling

Given the widespread availability of counselling, it is possibly the type of therapy that people living with dementia are most likely to experience. However, while there are many qualitative reports of counselling with people with dementia, including case studies (e.g., Clarke et al., 2016), there have been few structured trials. The largest and most methodologically sophisticated study to have reported its findings is the Danish Alzheimer's Disease Intervention Study or DAISY (Phung et al., 2013; Waldorf et al., 2012). DAISY involved a multi-faceted and semi-tailored support programme offered both to people who had been recently diagnosed with dementia and to their family carers. In this study 330 participating couples were allocated to receive either the intervention or to be in the control arm. The intervention consisted of a combination of counselling sessions (for the person with dementia on their own, for the carer alone, and for them together), an information and support group involving separate courses for participants and family caregivers and written information for both participants and caregivers. The primary aim of the intervention was to reduce levels of depression and to improve health-related quality of life in participants affected by dementia.

DAISY was an ambitious study as it compared the intervention and control groups for levels of depression after a year and adopted an extremely conservative level of $p < 0.0005$ for statistical probability, rather than the more usual level of $p < 0.05$. While methodologically correct as a way of controlling for the possibility of finding spurious effects from multiple testing, there are also arguments that as this was the main outcome measure it was not a necessary precaution. Indeed, although participants' depression levels improved and would have been significant at the normal level, these changes did not reach this enhanced level of significance that the authors used.

Recently, a UK-based study (Griffiths et al., 2021) used a type of qualitative research (framework analysis) to understand the experiences of individuals with dementia or caring for someone with dementia, before and after a 12-week relational counselling intervention. They carried out 29 semi-structured interviews with participants before they received the counselling and 25 after this intervention. Participants reported that counselling helped them to work through a range of needs and concerns that they had, enabling them to reassess and reconsider these. Importantly, both people living with dementia and their family carers described the strong emotional impact of the diagnosis, particularly in regard to the unknown trajectory of the dementia, the grief associated with actual and anticipated losses and a sense of helplessness or loss of self as someone living with dementia or caring for a relative with dementia. Both participant groups reported positive change post-counselling – with clients with dementia often valuing the counselling process in terms of acceptance and being able to 'move forward'.

Psychodynamic psychotherapy

Psychodynamic approaches have had a broad and important influence on dementia care (Evans et al., 2019). This influence can be seen in Miesen's framing of challenging behaviour as often reflecting the way that a person seeks to meet their attachment needs or to create a greater sense of security (e.g., Miesen, 2016) and in the influence of the unconscious on behaviour (e.g., Balfour 2006). I will describe both Miesen's and Balfour's work more fully in Chapter 5. However, psychodynamic research tends to be undertaken at a level that translates more easily into case studies (e.g., Davenhill, 2007) and finely argued observational reports (Evans, 2008, 2019) than into large-scale randomized trials. The qualitative nature of this work is, however, extremely useful for therapists by drawing attention to aspects of their work that they may otherwise not have attended to, including whether unconscious processing has affected their abilitiy to maintain boundaries around their work (Evans et al., 2019). Sinason (1992) addresses some of these boundary issues when she describes how working in a patient's home raised ethical concerns around the patient's right to consent to treatment. Her way of resolving this was to allow her patient some control over session times, so that if he was not ready for her, then she would return to see him at a later time or date. The ending of the work was precipitated by her awareness that her patient 'Edward Jackson' was not participating actively in the sessions as he had done and that he had effectively withdrawn from the sessions in order to invest his energies elsewhere.

Interpersonal therapies

The goal of interpersonal psychotherapy (IPT) is to help identify and resolve interpersonal difficulties that may be contributing to distress (Sukhawathanakul et al., 2021). Two studies with people living with dementia incorporated elements of psychodynamic interpersonal therapy. In the first study (Burns et al., 2005) 40 people with mild levels of cognitive impairment were randomized to either receive six 50-minute sessions of psychodynamic interpersonal therapy (PIT) or usual care. The authors did not find any significant differences on their main outcome measures. Unusually for research in this area, the second study to report the results of IPT (Carreira et al., 2008) also compared the impact of psychotherapy on people with and without a cognitive impairment. Carreira and colleagues conducted a sub-group analysis of a larger randomized controlled trial, or RCT, comparing maintenance of the medication paroxetine and IPT in participants aged 70 years of age or older who had depression. Their findings suggested that participants with cognitive impairment who received IPT fared significantly better than those participants in the control condition (relapsing on average after 58 weeks compared to 17 weeks). The authors suggested that IPT may have helped to resolve interpersonal conflict with caregivers in the cognitively impaired group.

Adapting therapy

All forms of psychotherapy, regardless of the therapeutic orientation that they derive from, will need to be adapted if they are to be delivered effectively with people with dementia. However, the type of adaptation will depend on the specific form of therapy being used. Perhaps the fullest account of how therapy can be adapted relates to the pilot trial of CBT that is described above (Charlesworth et al., 2015). While these adaptations relate specifically to a particular form of therapy, many of these are more widely applicable.

Taking advantage of the scaffolding inherent within CBT

CBT occurs within a clear and explicit structure, sometimes referred to as scaffolding, which potentially aids people with dementia in learning new techniques. This includes a recurring structure within sessions, establishing an agenda, goal setting, feedback and homework or 'take-home tasks'. By its nature, CBT also lends itself to incorporating cognitive rehabilitation strategies and techniques including the use of diaries and calendars.

Pacing

The therapist needs to work at an appropriate pace for the individual client and to take into account factors such as level of anxiety and cognitive impairment.

Within- and between-session strategies to support learning

This includes therapists using external memory aids, such as a folder for storing psycho-educational and self-monitoring materials, providing end-of-session summaries and making use of technologies such as smart phones.

Strategies to support memory

Therapists can encourage clients to put descriptions of helpful coping strategies in places where they can be easily seen, for instance on the fridge door. This can include strategies for 'pausing' thoughts associated with panic attacks, which might be captured through using key phrases such as *'Stop and think!'* and *'Slow it down'*.

Involving a 'supportive other'

The interventions involved both the person living with dementia and their carer, whose role was to act as a *'supportive other'* by providing memory prompts so that the client can generalize his or her learning from therapy into everyday life. As this involvement of another person into the therapeutic process can raise ethical issues, for instance around confidentiality, the boundaries of and expectations around therapy were discussed thoroughly before therapy began.

Supporting the learning of pre-therapy skills

Therapists actively set out to encourage those cognitive skills that are the precursors to effective therapy, including self-awareness. This includes using strategies for expanding emotional vocabulary and differentiating between thoughts, feelings and emotions.

Final words

Using psychotherapy with people living with dementia can be challenging. Therapists need to take into account not only the person's neurological impairment but also the emotional weight of their diagnosis and then create a safe therapeutic space to deliver therapy. As a consequence, all forms of individual therapy make use of family carers of the person living with dementia in one way or another – either to facilitate the practical arrangements for sessions or to act as co-therapists in some way. In the next chapter I will go on to consider another way of working with caregivers – by focusing on the relationship between caregivers and the person with dementia.

Whatever the advantages and disadvantages of any form of psychotherapy, the most obvious barrier that prevents its wider uptake is the paucity of resources available to support people after a diagnosis (Watts et al., 2014). For instance, in many UK community mental health teams, the profession that is most likely to provide a psychotherapy service is clinical psychology. However, while 200,000 people are expected to develop dementia each year in the UK, the membership of the Faculty of Psychology of Older People or FPOP, which is largely made up of those clinical psychologists working in the NHS with older people, comprises just 600 members. Of these, many psychologists will have multiple aspects to their roles that provide them with little opportunity to provide psychotherapy, while others may find it challenging to locate support and training.

While psychotherapy can of course be delivered by non-psychologists, the reality is that most people who are diagnosed with dementia will be unlikely to encounter therapy. In order to overcome this barrier to access, then, it is important that psychotherapy skills should be made as widely available as possible, for instance by psychologists offering training and support to their colleagues. In the following two chapters I will explore how psychologists working with couples and in groups have tried to build psychotherapy training and supervision into their practice.

5 Couples and family psychotherapy

When you meet someone living with dementia, in most cases you will also meet a member of their family, or friend who is providing care to them – a family carer. While there are around 900,000 people currently living with dementia in the UK, there are around 700,000 family carers (Alzheimer's Research UK, 2022a). The nature of cognitive impairment means that people become progressively more dependent on other people for help to complete even the most basic tasks of daily living, such as preparing meals, washing clothes and so on. In addition, a person's cognitive impairment will also impact on their ability to participate in therapy both in terms of their ability to attend (for instance a client may need to be prompted to remember an appointment or require support to travel to and from the session) and also to engage with therapy when they are present. Inevitably, then, as I have described in Chapter 4, psychotherapists need to adapt the content of their work to accommodate their client's cognitive impairment and often will do so by involving family caregivers in the therapeutic process in one way or another. While the precise nature of this involvement will vary depending on the type of therapy, and the extent of the person's impairment, finding a way to work with the person's supporters and carers is vital.

There are other ways, too, in which working with a carer is, in most cases, an essential element of therapeutic work. For many people living with dementia the experience of not being able to rely on themselves, in the sense of recalling even a basic chronology of recent events, means that being able to turn to another can be hugely reassuring. Indeed, as a person's cognitive impairment increases and the functional envelope of their life contracts, so the person's relationship with their carer becomes central to maintaining an emotional equilibrium. The way in which many people living with dementia respond to the insecurity that this brings is by holding close to the important person in their life – the person who provides security, familiarity and reassurance. In this way, partners can come to act as an attachment figure in the lives of the person with dementia – not just providing practical care, but also symbolizing their emotional security. The Dutch psychologist Bère Miesen traced some of these attachment experiences in his 2016 book *Dementia in Close-up*, identifying the way in which a person's attachment styles influence how the person living with dementia responds to the feelings of insecurity that dementia inevitably creates.

In his work, Miesen drew on the decades of psychological research exploring how people establish relationships with other people. The term '*attachment*' refers to a *'lasting psychological connectedness between human beings'* (Bowlby, 1969), and is often established during the person's earliest years through their relationship with their parents or others providing care. Because these parental or caregiving figures vary in their levels of sensitivity and responsiveness, and because each child has different needs, not all infants attach to caregivers in the same way. However, regardless of this, the young child begins to develop a set of expectations about how relationships work – about, for instance, how to express feelings of distress and whether or not others will respond to their behaviour. The different expectations and patterns of behaviour that children develop are referred to as different styles of attachment.

Research consistently suggests that the attachment styles that are developed during childhood extend into adult life, for instance, in patterns of romantic relationships, and that these are likely to be activated at times of stress (Feeney and Noller, 1990; Simpson and Rholes, 2017). Although there are different systems of categorizing and approaching these different styles, many researchers distinguish between three different patterns of behaviour: secure, ambivalent and avoidant attachment styles.

Miesen argued that there was evidence to show that people living with dementia responded to the insecurity that was inherent within their dementia in precisely the same ways that they had done throughout their life – that is through behaviour that was consistent with their attachment style. Thus, someone with a secure attachment style might look to their partner for reassurance, and be comforted by them, allowing their care needs to be attended to. A person with an ambivalent attachment style might be extremely anxious and preoccupied about separation, while a person with dementia whose behaviour could be characterized as avoidant would be more likely to refuse help, and to insist that this wasn't necessary. As the psychotherapist Andrew Balfour remarks: *'As adults we do not outgrow our need for security, and attachment encompasses the whole lifespan and is particularly relevant in dementia'* (Balfour, 2020, p.119).

Alongside these powerful practical and emotional reasons for involving family carers in the therapeutic process, there are often equally compelling reasons to be cautious in doing so. Firstly, any movement towards involvement of carers needs to be carefully managed to ensure that the boundaries around confidentiality are not compromised. While family members may be understandably concerned about how their relative is responding to their dementia, it is vital that therapists protect the privacy of the sessions. Secondly, dementia will be superimposed on a previous relationship in which patterns of relating will have grown and developed often over many years. While many healthcare professionals are trained to respond to a 'patient' and a 'carer', in the initial stages of dementia these can be rather artificial constructs. Instead, people with dementia and their partners typically continue to define themselves as a couple or as a family (Quinn et al., 2009) and face dementia in precisely the same ways that they have done with other challenges in their life together. In some cases, people will sit down and come to a collective decision about how to proceed. For other couples, the best way to cope may be to carry on as if nothing has happened. Each couple, just like each person, will find their own, unique way to cope.

The third reason why it is important – where possible – to involve families and couples in the therapeutic process is that just as the attachment style of the person living with dementia will impact on how they respond to the insecurity that it engenders, so the attachment style of a family carer will also play a role in how they respond to the distress of their partner (Kokkonen et al., 2014). One study of 116 married couples where one spouse was living with dementia found that the attachment styles of partners were significantly associated both to each other and to different behavioural interactions (Perren et al., 2007). For instance, where caregivers had an avoidant attachment style and care recipients an insecure attachment style, they found that there were also more likely to be increased levels of dementia-related challenging behaviour. The authors suggested that this may have been due to the person with dementia responding to heightened feelings of insecurity by seeking greater closeness – which may have resulted in avoidant caregivers seeking a greater degree of distancing. This, in turn, may have been experienced as a rejection by the person living with dementia, precipitating appeals for greater intimacy and reassurance.

Finally, the nature of the relationship between a person with dementia and their family carer will inevitably be complicated as dementia impacts on them differently. In many ways, dementia acts to heighten strains that may already exist within relationships. Thus, if a partner comes to represent security to the person with dementia, then they also symbolize their dependency. If they become the practical carriers of a person's memory, then in so doing they are also reminders of an acquired incompetence and while partners witness the deterioration of the person living with dementia, they may also survive it. These complicated patterns of emotional response can take the form of recurring reciprocal patterns in which couples and families move around each other. For instance, the person with dementia may hide their knowledge of dementia in order to protect their spouse who may then avoid referring to dementia in order not to shame their partner. Alternatively, the person with dementia may seek to lessen the emotional weight of their dementia by projecting out their failures onto their family carer, effectively making the 'other' into the problem.

Given, then, that when we work therapeutically with a person living with dementia, we are also highly likely to be working with a family carer, then the choice that we have to make is not *whether* to work with this dyad, but rather *how* we should work. For many therapists, the focus of work becomes seeking to repair, or to at least ameliorate, the impact of dementia on the relationship between the person with dementia and their carer. This approach contrasts with the therapeutic work that I described in the last chapter which, while it may have involved working with family carers, nevertheless framed this as a way of facilitating therapeutic work with the person with dementia.

There is some evidence, albeit inconsistent, that supportive marital relationships may well have a material effect on the course of dementia (Norton et al., 2009) and on the development of challenging behaviour (Edwards et al., 2018).

Wright, for instance, found that for 30 couples, unhappy marital relationships at the start of her study were associated with placement in a nursing home two years later (Wright, 1994; Wright et al., 1995). Similarly, other studies have found evidence that providing family caregivers with emotional support earlier on significantly delayed subsequent admission to residential care of the person with dementia (Brodaty et al., 1997; Mittelman et al., 2006).

Working with couples also enables any latent tensions within a relationship to be addressed. For instance, the longevity of a couples' relationship may background their collective response to dementia. If a couple have been together a long time, then there is '*plenty in the bank*' in terms of a partner having an unconscious sense that their time and commitment has been '*earnt*' in some way (Suzanne Davis, personal communication). However, where couples have met relatively late in their lives, then feelings of resentment at having to care for the other person can impact on the relationship. In these circumstances, it can be important in couples work to acknowledge this so that decisions about future care can be deliberately and consciously taken.

Couples therapy

Just as is the case with psychotherapy that focuses on the needs of the person with dementia, so reports of couples therapy have grown significantly in recent years. However, two recent reviews of the literature (Bielsten and Hellström, 2019a; 2019b) and a third, slightly older review (Benbow and Sharman, 2014) have all pointed out some important weaknesses in the literature. Importantly, joint interventions for people with dementia and care partners were thought to lack a genuine dyadic approach which valued both partners' views of their relationship equally (Bielsten and Hellström, 2019a) and in some cases disregarded the views of the person with dementia (Bielsten and Hellström, 2019b). There were also more general challenges around how techniques from family therapy could be made more widely available, for instance by training the wider health and social care workforce to work effectively with families (Benbow and Sharman, 2014).

Living together with dementia

One approach to couples therapy that addressed the need identified in Bielsten and Hellström's reviews of spreading psychological skills into the wider dementia workforce was the Living Together with Dementia project led by Andrew Balfour at the Tavistock Centre for Couple Relationships (Balfour, 2014; 2020). Living Together with Dementia (or LTwD) focused on the person living with dementia and their partner together, concentrating on the relationship between them. For Balfour, problems arise not just because of the trauma of diagnosis, and the difficulties of adjusting to the illness, but also because negative cycles of interaction arise within the relationship resulting in a secondary disablement. This refers to the way in which people gradually lose the capacity to carry out daily activities and become increasingly dependent. For many couples, their relationship risks losing those protective qualities that buffers each of them against psychological distress. Replacing these protective elements involves improving emotional contact, building a mutual understanding of the challenges that dementia creates for them as a couple and using shared interactions to create positive interactions between partners.

The LTwD approach sought to promote resilience within relationships and thus to restore some of the protective aspects of the relationship. It did this by supporting the person with dementia to maintain their engagement with their partner by asking them to collaborate together on everyday activities, finding strategies for both partners to become more interdependent and addressing the challenge of social isolation and its adverse mental and physical health consequences. Importantly LTwD sought to provide support to both partners in adjusting to the diagnosis and to contain their emotional responses to this.

The structure and sequence of sessions within the LTwD programme followed a consistent pattern and consisted of eight to ten sessions spread over the course of several months. Individual therapy sessions with each partner occurred regularly throughout, with alternate weeks spent either videotaping a new activity or reviewing the video recorded in the previous session. Each session ended with a psychotherapeutic discussion including both partners together. As well as being delivered by counselling and clinical psychologists, a range of professionals working in the mental health and social and voluntary care sector were trained to deliver LTwD, including occupational therapists, social workers and nurses, and received supervision from Andrew and his team. The intervention itself was manualized (Balfour, 2014).

Drawing on a video-based coaching technique which was originally developed for people with autism and their parents (Gutstein and Sheely, 2002), LTwD therapists worked with couples to highlight the way in which they communicated and interacted. Couples were recorded carrying out an everyday activity which they then reviewed in the following session with the therapist paying attention to the emotional contact between them. This encouraged couples to see their interactions in a fresh and less rigid way than before and in so doing helped them to build an understanding of each other's experiences and to experiment with new ways of communicating. They began to question or become interested in why things were happening between them in a particular way.

Using video recordings to help couples affected by dementia distinguishes the LTwD project from other forms of psychotherapy in the UK. However, in this regard psychotherapy with people with dementia in the UK is catching up with clinical practice in mental health services for children and families and for people with learning disabilities where these techniques have been used for some time. Similarly, dementia care practitioners in Scandinavia and the Netherlands have used Marte Meo video guidance or counselling to help care workers to gain an empathic appreciation of the needs of residents with dementia (Gudex et al., 2008; Alnes et al., 2011a). Nurses in these studies reported that Marte Meo counselling helped them to gain a better understanding of the residents, for instance being better able to interpret their expressions, and enabled them to recognize how their own behaviour impacted upon residents (Alnes et al., 2011b). For instance, nurses became aware of the importance of pacing their interactions according to the impairments of residents, maintaining eye contact and talking to residents while they were providing care.

The LTwD project combined therapeutic use of video recording with an emphasis on using psychotherapy to help both the person with dementia and their partner to process the emotional distress arising from dementia. For this to happen, the emotional distress of both parties needs to be contained by another. Typically, it is the family carer who is the main source of containment for the person with dementia – someone who can tolerate the emotions being projected into them without reacting punitively or by withdrawing. Yet, for the carer to continue in this role effectively, then their own emotional distress must also be contained. The role of the LTwD therapist is to be '*a third containing figure … who the care partner is able to talk to about the reality of their feelings, who is not going to judge but who will listen*' (Balfour and Salter, 2018, p. 195). The therapist acts to '*contain the container*' (Balfour, 2020, p.127). Balfour likens this phenomenon to a series of dolls of different sizes, each nesting within another: the person with dementia is contained by their partner, who is contained by the therapist, who in turn themselves has their emotions contained within supervision.

Some support for this perspective on therapy comes from the doctoral thesis of a counselling psychologist, Beth Winter, who I supervised. In her qualitative study, Beth spoke with a series of couples who had received LTwD (Winter, 2020). One family carer, Lara, described how important it had been to have a space in which she felt understood ('*somebody I could talk to, I think and understands…understands what you're sort of going through*') while others described therapy helping them to make sense of events and their feelings and to be honest about the impact of caring. LTwD participants with dementia also described being able to use the therapy to make sense out of what was happening to them. Thus, Peggy described her dementia as being '*very confusing, like very different, and it's very, very scary what happens to you. That was quite uh, scary. It's a horrible feeling of not being — I know you can't control your dreams either, but not being in charge of, what you're actually doing and, not understanding half of it*'. Other participants with dementia valued the therapeutic relationship, with Martha describing her therapist as being: '*good. She makes you feel quite relaxed. And she is good company… I think a lot of it was her personality. She made people feel at ease… But it's nice to think that someone's remembered that you have got this. You do feel quite lonely… This is a sort of a mysterious illness, isn't it?*'.

While the LTwD project provides a powerful beacon of good practice, nevertheless for many psychotherapists it requires too high a level of resources in terms of training and access to video recording for it to become embedded in everyday practice. However, in my experience it is possible for therapists to adapt psychotherapy techniques from a range of different modalities to try to achieve precisely the same goals as LTwD – namely to help the person with dementia and their family carer to adjust to the challenges that dementia creates for their relationship. The case example of David and Clare illustrates just such a way of working.

David and Claire: Meeting attachment needs[1]

Over the years I have worked in dementia care I have provided clinical supervision to my colleagues – a space where we discuss their work and reflect on both how the therapy is going, and the impact that this is having on them. I will refer to one of these psychologists as Sarah Green – an accomplished therapist who had worked in dementia care throughout her career. One of Sarah's clients, David Philipps, had been diagnosed with Alzheimer's disease at the age of 73, a year before he was referred to her. The community psychiatric nurse in her team who made the referral asked for Sarah's advice to help David and his wife Claire to manage his recurring panic attacks and anxiety.

When Sarah met the couple, they described how he had been feeling increasingly worried for some time and that this had affected his behaviour in many ways, for instance by making himself vomit almost every day as a way, he told her, of '*controlling my nerves*'. David told Sarah that he had always been an anxious person and that he had never felt '*competent*' in life. Since the diagnosis he had come to feel empty inside and felt that he did not have a purpose, lacking a role and missing both his old job and being able to drive himself. During this assessment David didn't acknowledge his dementia, instead focusing on his anger and distress at being banned from driving.

David's relationship with Claire had become more complicated after the diagnosis. She seemed to Sarah to be a very competent and composed woman. David often referred to her as '*Mum*', while on her part she described caring for David now as akin to '*having a child*'. David found even short absences from her very upsetting, for instance if Claire was in another part of their house and out of his sight. When this happened, he would search for her and, if he could not quickly find her, then this often triggered a panic attack. David also ruminated on the thought that Claire would die before him, leaving him on his own.

Claire described her frustration at how their relationship had changed. She felt they were now caught in a pattern of behaviour where David insisted that she do everything for him yet then blamed her when something went wrong. Claire told Sarah privately that she felt that she couldn't continue to cope with David, and that unless his behaviour changed, then she would need to find him a place in a nursing home.

---

1 The names of psychotherapists and their clients contained in this and other case studies have been altered.

For Sarah, aspects of David's behaviour were consistent with an ambivalent attachment style and suggested an underlying sense of insecurity. According to Claire, David's lifelong tendency to be emotionally needy had been intensified by the diagnosis, which he would not discuss, and by his struggles to complete tasks. David craved the reassurance he gained from Claire's presence, but this was undermined by the thought of her leaving him. Additionally, David's reluctance to acknowledge his dementia and growing cognitive impairments meant that as a couple they were not able to discuss how these were contributing to the changes in their relationship. Sarah felt that David resented his reliance on Claire and instead projected out his neediness onto her causing him to be so critical of her. He blamed Claire for the problems his dementia caused, while she was frustrated at his neediness.

At the end of her assessment, Sarah wrote the couple a preliminary formulation letter where she laid out her initial thoughts about how the problems that they were facing had developed, and a possible way forward for them both. Sarah then read the formulation letter to them both and asked for their response to it. In the letter she framed David's lack of confidence as adding to the very real problems he was experiencing – for instance it led to him avoiding thinking about the causes of his poor memory. While they were both coping as well as they could with the dementia, they were coping as individuals, rather than as a couple.

The most immediate focus of their work used cognitive behaviour therapy techniques to address his anxiety. Together Sarah worked with David and Claire to set a series of incremental targets for spending time apart, starting with Claire being just out of David's eyesight, but nevertheless still able to talk with him, and then moving gradually further and further away. Sarah suggested that as a couple they could learn to use controlled breathing to manage his anxiety which they supported using simple visual aids to prompt relaxation.

Later, Sarah encouraged David to rethink his negative interpretations: for instance, she challenged his fears of Claire dying before him by pointing out that Claire was healthy and that even if his worst fears were realized then there would be other sources of emotional support that he could draw on. As their work progressed, so David was able to reflect on how his fears about Claire dying were similar to those he had had as a child about his mother – and reassured himself by remembering that he had been able to cope when she eventually passed away.

While this work progressed, Sarah talked with David and Claire about the changes in their lives. They reflected on how they had first noticed that something was wrong with his memory, and the journey they had taken to his diagnosis. Sarah used circular questioning as a way of helping the couple to reflect on both their own feelings about the dementia, and their beliefs about how their partner felt. They identified particular trigger points, including Claire's responses to David's memory lapses, which he sometimes experienced as rather patronizing. Together they agreed more helpful responses.

Over time David grew in confidence, becoming less anxious and managing his feelings without making himself sick every day. Some of the tensions between David and Claire were resolved, as he reduced the demands he made on Claire, and was more able to calm himself. Although David was still concerned when Claire was out of his sight, as a couple they had worked out ways of recognizing and responding to this and consequently they both saw David's distress as much less of a problem for them. David was now able to talk about dementia, although he still found this painful, and he no longer asked to drive his car. Claire said that she felt that the therapy sessions had helped David to be more tolerant of himself and consequently less confused and muddled. She no longer felt that he would need to be admitted to a nursing home.

As Sarah contemplated ending therapy, so it was clear that David in particular would find this difficult. Their regular therapy sessions were extremely comforting to him, and in some senses, aspects of his emotional reliance on Claire had transferred to Sarah. For her part, Sarah felt burdened by this and in supervision we discussed her sense of tension between her wish to be important in people's lives, and the enormity of assuming this responsibility. Sarah spoke with David and Claire about ending therapy, and as a compromise they agreed to meet initially every three weeks and for the period between sessions to gradually lengthen.

Final words

For the most part, when psychotherapists work with someone living with dementia, they do not simply have a choice of *whether* they work with the person's partner or carer. Instead, the decision they face is *how* to work with this relationship – that is whether or not to focus on change at an individual level or within the relationship itself. Over the course of my career, I increasingly worked with couples together about the dementia – encouraging them, just as Sarah Green did, to talk about the impact that the condition was having on them as a couple.

One of the main reasons that I started to work in this way was that many couples rarely seemed to talk about what was happening to them – partly I suspect because they were often too busy coping with the everyday problems that life threw at them. However, there was another reason why couples did not make time in their lives: often both partners wanted to protect the other one, and indeed themselves, from distress. When this happened, then, sometimes the unattended dementia would come to act as a barrier between them. Misunderstandings would arise, and while there was greater tension in their relationship, neither felt able to start to talk about what was happening to them. They did not know where, or how, to begin talking. The simple act of asking each of them, in each other's presence, about how dementia was affecting themselves and their partner would often help to bring couples together – in much the same way that Andrew Balfour has described LTwD as helping to restore psychological resilience within couples. Working with the relationship between couples in therapy, then, can have a power and reach beyond what is often possible in individual therapy – it can enhance the process by which people come to terms with their dementia. In the next chapter I will turn to another way of augmenting therapy – by using the power of one's peers in group therapy.

6　Group psychotherapy

The most likely way that people who are living with dementia will encounter psychotherapy will be by being part of a group (Cheston, 1998). For a few this will be by being part of a specific psychotherapy group. For many others, however, psychotherapy will be encountered incidentally when they are part of a support or psychoeducation group. While these groups do not explicitly aim to provide psychotherapy, many aspects of the work that is carried out is nevertheless inherently therapeutic. For instance, support groups meet regularly, are exclusively for participants who share a common condition and aim to facilitate people talking about their shared experiences. As I will describe below, this constitutes what Yalom has described as *'universality'* – an important therapeutic factor within any form of group work (e.g., Yalom and Leszcz, 2020). Thus, regardless of what label a group is tagged with – whether this is for 'support', or for 'education' – I believe that it is legitimate to consider them as 'being' psychotherapeutic so long as they contain at least some of these therapeutic factors. Indeed, this is still the case even if their facilitators would not necessarily consider themselves as 'doing' psychotherapy.

At the same time, however, I do not want to ignore the many differences that exist between different types of groups. Some therapeutic approaches, for instance, place relatively little emphasis on group dynamics and instead view groups as an efficient way to provide therapy. The format of a cognitive behavioural therapy group, for instance, is likely to be roughly the same as an individual programme. In contrast, group analytic psychotherapies explicitly use the interpersonal relationships that develop within the group as the medium through which therapy occurs (e.g., Cheston et al., 2003). As I will outline below, being part of a group brings with it therapeutic possibilities and advantages that may be of particular relevance for people who are living with dementia. For instance, groups composed solely of participants who are living with dementia may be in a unique position to challenge myths around dementia, and to reduce some of the shame-filled burden of stigma that participants experience.

Group therapeutic factors

The process by which groups achieve their therapeutic impact is difficult to define precisely and has as a consequence been defined variously as 'curative factors' (Butler and Fuhriman, 1983) and 'mechanisms of change' (Fonagy and Bateman, 2006). Perhaps the most well-known framework is that of Irvin Yalom who identified 12 therapeutic factors (Yalom and Leszcz, 2020). Among these, several factors are especially relevant when considering the psychological needs of people living with dementia. Appreciating these potent mechanisms may help group therapists to identify them as they occur in therapy and to find strategies to enhance their impact on the group.

Universality

Given the barriers that prevent people living with dementia from talking about their illness in public, it is unsurprising that some feel that they are on their own. Attending a therapy group with one's peers – all of whom are united by the fact that they share a diagnosis- and then talking openly about that defining characteristic can be a powerful antidote to this isolation. One participant in a LivDem group that I will describe below, for instance, summarized the impact of the group on her in this way: '*I didn't realize there were others in the same situation as me. I felt quite alone before the group*'. Another participant responded in a similar way: the course provides '*a forum where everyone is equal – everyone has dementia and knows what you're experiencing*'. Not only does a group provide participants with tangible evidence that they are not the only people to have these experiences, but in so doing it also normalizes the person's responses to their dementia. As Mr B, a participant in the Dementia Voice group psychotherapy project (Watkins et al., 2006) commented: '*I thought, well, I'm going mad, I'm going crazy. What am I going to be like in another five years? But now I realize that everybody is getting this problem*'.

It is important to add a note of caution here. Dementia care is full of examples in which people living with dementia are gathered together. In principle, these could all provide opportunities to enhance a sense of universality and for participants to come to see themselves as part of a wider community. However, all too often the very thing that brings people together – their dementia – is not spoken about. As I have described in the first part of this book, it can feel as if it is taboo to talk about the dementia. This extends not just to an avoidance of mentioning a specific diagnosis but also to a reluctance to explore the significance of any of the symptoms of the dementia even when these occur in a session, for instance if participants forget each other's names or need help to pour themselves a cup of tea. This failure to acknowledge the 'demon' of dementia even when participants can feel its hot breath on the back of their necks is not just a missed therapeutic opportunity but is positively anti-therapeutic – because it adds to the sense that dementia is too frightening, too awful, too intimidating to even name.

Altruism

The progressive cognitive impairment inherent in all forms of dementia not only reduces a person's independence, but it also restricts opportunities for them to help or to support others. As a series of social psychological accounts have indicated, these changes in role impact on self-functioning and steadily degrade a person's identity (Sabat, 2002; Sabat et al., 2004). Within a group, however, people with dementia become by default experts by experience, acting as a resource that others within the group can draw on. Groups can be quintessentially human places, with opportunities to console and advise, to empathize and chastise, to laugh and flirt. Participants gain through giving, as an intrinsic aspect of the act of giving is that the person has value to others.

Interpersonal learning input and output

The impact of their cognitive impairment on a participant's ability to function within a group setting will vary from one group member to another. For some, lapses in short-term memory lead them to repeat particular sentiments or phrases, while for others their impairment makes it harder for them to express or follow the conversation. For many people with dementia, the group may act as the first opportunity for accurate interpersonal feedback. This, however, needs to be sensitively handled – drawing attention to a deficit caused by the dementia may be construed as a criticism. However, if the facilitator fails to acknowledge the impact of cognitive impairments within the group, then this can also become a problem and the group may interpret it as a sign that dementia as a whole cannot be discussed.

Advice and guidance

As well as providing mutual support, groups can also be a venue for information about dementia to be provided, increasing participants' knowledge of the condition and challenging misconceptions. As I will set out in Part 3, an aspect of the adjustment process to dementia involves people being curious about their illness – for instance by asking who Alzheimer was, or what the word 'dementia' actually means. At other times, providing factual information, for instance, about the legal requirements around notifying the driving authorities following a diagnosis can prompt the group to acknowledge differences in the experiences of members. In this way, providing advice, when done at the appropriate time, can promote group participants to take decisions about their life and thus facilitate adjustment.

Catharsis

The open expression of affect is vital to the group therapeutic process; in its absence, a group would degenerate into a sterile academic exercise. Within the safety of a group, participants who are living with dementia may cry at their losses, rage at the unfairness of life, or envy those who are still able to do the things that they cannot. For facilitators it is important to allow all of these emotions to be expressed and to use this productively. When emotions are expressed, then they need to be acknowledged, contained and validated – preferably by others within the group, but if not then by the therapists.

Talking about dementia is inextricably bound up with a person's feelings about dementia. As participants begin to talk about what has happened to them, so they also begin to experience the emotions around this. In response to the emotional disequilibrium this causes, so there is a tendency for participants to move away from their dementia, thus restoring an emotional balance. Consequently, conversations about dementia move to and away from engaging with the feelings that this engenders (Snow et al., 2015). If the movement away from the dementia is continual and perhaps unhelpful – for instance if a group participant minimizes the impact of dementia on them – then the therapist may choose to remember the distress and to reflect it back in a digested form to the group. Thus, the therapeutic task at this point is to hold on to the distress that has been expressed for the group, and to bring it back to the group when they are ready to hear it again (Cheston, 2013).

Existential factors

As I have described in Part 1, dementia embodies an existential threat: not only is it an incurable illness, but it also threatens the core aspects of a person's identity, challenges the most important relationships in their lives and reduces almost all aspects of a person's functioning. Not only will participants have to struggle with those changes that have already taken place, but they will need to face the changes that are to come. While we can, and indeed must, frame dementia as an illness that people can live well with, we must also recognize that there will be no escape from deterioration and, ultimately, death. Groups can provide a safe, containing environment within which participants can explore the existential aspects of their dementia, as Mrs H explained in the Dementia Voice group psychotherapy project (Watkins et al., 2006): 'Not having all my faculties, I dread that, I dread that, it's as if I'm going to sort of come to it one morning, perhaps, you know and think, "Oh my godfathers, what's left?" You know I really worry about that'. For Yalom, the acknowledgement of the existential reality of life and facing the basic issues of life and death in an honest and open way means that one is less caught up in the trivialities and incidental concerns of life. For people living with dementia, openly putting a name to their fears within a supportive, containing space can enable them to find some emotional distance from these fears – a process that I will address in more detail in Part 3 of this book.

Instillation of hope

People take part in a group, indeed in any therapeutic activity, at least partly out of an expression of hope – hope that attending the group may be worthwhile and that something may change. In recruiting participants for a group, it is therefore important that the therapist reinforces positive expectations, corrects negative preconceptions, and presents a lucid and powerful explanation of the group's potential for change. During the group, therapists can underline and highlight the successes of participants in changing – and in doing so emphasize to participants that dementia can be lived with.

For people with dementia, one qualitative study suggested that the expression of hope can fall into two related areas: *'living in hope or dying in despair'* and *'keep living and keep living well'* (Wolverson et al., 2010). Thus, participants talked about a legacy of hope, instilled in them as children, which had been internalized into a character trait. Hope, too, became embodied within their partner, carer or family. While participants in this study expressed their sorrow at what they had lost, they were also reconciled to the prospect that their condition would not improve and that they were not going to 'get better'. At the same time, participants were also able to embrace new hopes and find new ways of being in the world in which they had made peace with their position. For some participants this took the form of being content with their current life that was both meaningful and rich. Half the group explicitly stated that they were happy, and others felt that they could not complain about their current situations since others were 'worse off' than them. For group therapists, then, helping participants to express and to acknowledge their hope is an important aspect of group work – and one which may well help people to adjust to their dementia (Cotter et al., 2018).

Group work: The evidence base

The review of the literature that I carried out with Ada Ivanecka (Cheston and Ivanecka, 2017) identified a series of well-designed and resourced studies using group therapy, all of which were aimed at people with mild to moderate levels of cognitive impairment. Of these, the strongest evidence to support group work comes from the Early-Stage Memory Loss Support (ESML) group study, which was carried out in the US (Logsdon et al., 2007, 2010). The ESML intervention involved nine weekly group sessions in which family members attended the first part of the group and drew on an established body of previous research (e.g., Snyder et al., 1995; Yale, 1995; Snyder et al., 2007). Unlike many other studies of psychotherapy with people living with dementia, this study was appropriately powered to find significant differences – that is to say it included enough participants to allow us to be confident that the study's findings would be valid. In all, 96 participants with mild or moderate levels of impairment were randomized to attend the ESML groups while another 46 were randomly allocated to the usual care condition. After controlling for baseline differences and changes in cognition, the authors reported significant improvements in two areas for participants at the end of the study: their quality of life had increased, while their scores on a measure of depression had reduced. Interestingly, those people who had the highest levels of emotional distress at the start of the groups seemed to benefit most from the group support that they received. However, while this study was able to compare participants' psychological functioning before and after the intervention, they did not carry out a follow-up assessment, so we have no way of knowing whether people who attended the ESML group continued to do well once the intervention had ended.

Together with Ann Marshall, a clinical psychologist working in Hampshire, and a team from the University of Southampton, I carried out a similar study to the ESML group, albeit on a smaller scale and in the UK (Marshall et al., 2015). The Living Well with Dementia or LivDem intervention, had similar inclusion criteria, session length and number of sessions to the ESML. However, while ESML sessions were provided by three or four trained and experienced facilitators, at least two of whom were master's level professionals, the LivDem therapists were nurses, occupational therapists and psychology assistants who had attended a two-day training course that Ann and I provided, but who otherwise had little or no experience of therapy. After adjusting for baseline differences between the two groups, we found a non-significant trend for improvements in self-esteem and quality of life in the intervention arm, with an effect size similar to that of Logsdon et al. (2010). Since that study, together with Emily Dodd at the University of the West of England, Ann and I have continued to develop LivDem, and have carried out other research studies to look at whether the way in which people talk about their dementia changes over the course of the study (see box below). The project is also supported through a website: https://www.livdem.co.uk/.

The *Living Well with Dementia (LivDem)* course

What is LivDem?

LivDem is an eight-week course aimed at people who have been diagnosed with Alzheimer's disease or another form of dementia in the relatively recent past. The course takes a deliberately slow pace, initially focusing on the symptoms of cognitive impairment, then the emotional impact of this and ways in which participants cope with their feelings. Only in the middle sessions, when the group has formed and is ready to discuss more emotionally threatening material do course facilitators introduce questions around talking about the diagnosis with others and look at the diagnosis, its treatment and prognosis. Finally, the LivDem course looks at ways of living well with dementia, including how participants can make decisions about the future, and the importance of staying as active as possible. Sessions last for 90 minutes and are led by two facilitators, who draw on a manual (Cheston and Marshall, 2019) and who will have received training, either from the LivDem team in person or online, or locally.

Emily Dodd and I have collected testimonies both from course facilitators, and also from LivDem course participants and their families through a combination of online surveys for course facilitators and post-course evaluations from different courses. This evidence suggests that there is a process of change that some, but by no means all, people who attend the LivDem course experience.

Firstly, participants realize that they are not alone and comment to course facilitators with statements such as: '*It was tremendously valuable to meet people in similar circumstances and to share experiences. It was like a control mechanism to help release how you are feeling*' and '*I didn't realize there were others in the same situation as me. I felt quite alone before the group*'.

Secondly, some participants report that they feel less frightened about their dementia: '*It made the diagnosis less scary*', '*I'm not so frightened of the future as I was beforehand*' and '*We are able to cope and get on with it. It's less frightening now*'. Thirdly, many participants say that they feel more confident about themselves and more able to tell other people about their dementia: '*I've been able to tell people about having dementia and been given the confidence to do that*', '*I now tell people "I have dementia" I haven't got a problem with it now*', '*It wasn't until I came to the group that I realized – just tell them*', and '*I now feel that the best thing to do is to tell friends that you have dementia and not be afraid of it*'.

These changes in how people talk about their dementia have been supported by two studies in which we first transcribed and then analysed recordings from the LivDem course. What this showed us was that there was an important change in the way people living with dementia talked about themselves. In the initial sessions, the main way in which people referred to dementia was indirectly and without actually naming it. Instead, they talked about '*it*' or '*that thing that I have*'. By the end of the course, participants were more likely to openly acknowledge and name their dementia and talked about their illness in a more emotionally connected and thoughtful way (Cheston et al., 2017). It may be that these changes reflect, in part, the fact that the slow, evolving pace of a LivDem course means that course facilitators gradually introduce more direct language about dementia as sessions progress. However, our research also suggests that where course facilitators used active listening skills to encourage discussion among participants then this promoted a greater openness. Thus, it appears that it is not simply that changes in the way in which people talk about their dementia are simply related to the course syllabus but that they are also a function of facilitators being more empathic and using simple counselling techniques such as reflective listening (Cheston et al., 2018b). I will explore this issue in more depth in Part 3.

The fourth aspect of the therapeutic process that LivDem participants describe is feeling that they have adjusted to their dementia in some way and begun to come to terms with it. Thus, in their post-evaluation feedback participants have stated: '*Before attending the group, I did not accept that I had this condition. Since attending I have accepted it and come to terms with it*' and '*I have realized this isn't the end … but the beginning*'.

Finally, some people feel that they are able to translate these changes into behaving in a new way and making some practical changes in their lives: '*I feel more confident and want to do more e.g., outings, simple chores*', '*It's given me a new lease of life*', '*I am now doing more and reading more, going out instead of sitting at home watching tv. It's livened me up a bit'*, and *'The group gave me time to think about how I would manage my frustration about forgetting things. I have learned not to get narky with myself about it'*. The family carer of a LivDem participant in Northampton commented, *'Most importantly the group halted a decline into "closing down" life, so life is opening up. We are looking at what is possible as opposed to what has been lost'*. Another carer in Sussex said, *'My husband looked forward to the sessions and felt secure and valued. Thank you for reopening some doors for us and giving us confidence to maximize what we have'*.

Final words

Working with a group of people, regardless of whether they have a cognitive impairment or not, requires both different skills and a different approach than are needed in either individual or couple therapy. Being part of a group provokes powerful emotions. The group has a life of its own that is separate from any single individual member – and which relates not only to the overt subject matter being discussed in the group but also to the experience of being part of a larger collective. In group analytic terms, this is known as the group matrix – a concept that is often attributed to the British therapist S. H. Foulkes (Roberts, 1982). The group becomes an entity in itself – behaving in a way that is analogous to a hive mind, a network of conscious and unconscious communications that requires the group therapists to respond (or not to respond). For a group of people who are all living with dementia, the group as a whole has to find a way to talk about dementia – the unifying characteristic that has brought them together. It is this subject, how we talk to people about dementia, whether this is in the context of individual, couples or group psychotherapy that I will now turn to in Part 3 of this book.

Summary of Part 2: Psychotherapy in practice

Using psychotherapy with people living with dementia can be challenging. Therapists need to take into account not only the person's neurological impairment but also the emotional weight of their diagnosis and then create a safe therapeutic space to deliver therapy. While there are accounts of using almost all forms of therapy with people living with dementia, the evidence base is still emerging and limits the conclusions that can be drawn. While there are good arguments to be made for both individual and couples therapy, the strongest evidence for the usefulness of psychotherapy suggests that support groups can help to reduce distress and improve quality of life, especially in the earlier stages of dementia. For a group of people who are all living with dementia, the group as a whole has to find a way to talk about dementia – the unifying characteristic that has brought them together.

Implications for people living with dementia

Many people living with dementia may not have considered seeking out a psychotherapist or counsellor. However, there are good reasons for doing just this so people living with dementia should think about the following points.

- Talking with a trained therapist may help them to make sense of their feelings and to feel more in control of their life. It may help them to feel less frightened by their dementia, to recognize that they are not alone, and help them to be more open about their condition.

Implications for family carers

People who are caring for someone with dementia should think about the following points.

- Consider finding time to talk about the dementia. It is often difficult for couples and families to make time in their lives to talk about dementia – often both partners want to protect the other one, and indeed themselves, from distress. It can also be difficult to know what to say.
- Couples should consider looking for a therapist or counsellor who can provide time to listen and to help them to reflect on how dementia is affecting them both and their relationship.

- Think about whether they also need time to emotionally process what they are going through, as well as thinking about the impact of this on the person that they are caring for.

Implications for therapists

Healthcare professionals whose job involves offering specific counselling or psychotherapy sessions should think about the following points.

- Therapists need to decide how to involve family carers of the person living with dementia within therapy – either to facilitate the practical arrangements for sessions or to act as co-therapists in some way. Without the tacit agreement and often the active collaboration from family carers, therapy will be difficult to sustain.
- Therapists should routinely draw upon experienced colleagues for support, training and supervision when working with people living with dementia – and where relevant look to offer this themselves to their co-workers.

Implications for dementia care workers

Staff working in dementia care should think about the following points.

- In order to increase access to psychotherapy, it is important that psychotherapy skills, and especially active listening skills, should be widely used within all dementia services.
- Working with people living with dementia is often a complex process – and this is especially the case when looking to support people using psychotherapy or counselling skills. Dementia care workers should actively seek out opportunities for supervision and support.

Part 3

Becoming the same, but different

Adjusting to (and talking about) dementia

So far, in outlining how psychotherapy has been used with people living with dementia, I have focused on the techniques of psychotherapy, and have avoided looking in any detail either at the underlying process of adjustment or at the wider psychotherapeutic process. In this part of the book, I will turn to just these issues and set out my understanding of the way in which therapists can help people with dementia to talk more openly about their dementia – and in this way, help them to adjust to it. In equating talking about dementia with adjustment to the condition, I will follow an old axiom within therapy that equates thinking (and hence adjusting) with talking – *'I don't know what I think until I hear what I say'*. This quotation has a long and rather uncertain background, being used by the British writer, E.M. Forster and sometimes attributed to the French author André Gide. Its meaning, however, is straightforward. Talking and thinking are intertwined. Talking about a complex issue enables us to make sense of it. Talking allows us to process the meaning of an event and its impact on us. It helps people to remember what is happening, and to bring their thoughts to bear on it.

In this way, talking about dementia makes the dementia real – it is a fundamental part of the way in which people adjust to it. However, there is a problem. Talking about dementia is often difficult. As I argued in the opening chapters of this book, talking about dementia provokes powerful feelings including those around fear, loss and shame. There are good reasons, then, not to talk – good reasons why people choose not to make the dementia real by talking about it. Therefore, before people are able to talk about dementia, they have to feel that it is safe for them to do so. And helping people to feel safe enough to talk about their dementia is a core therapeutic task.

7 Adjustment

In Part 2, I outlined how psychotherapy has been used to address the psychological needs of people living with dementia. I emphasized that all forms of therapy needed to be adapted to accommodate the cognitive impairments and changed circumstances of clients living with dementia. However, I omitted to consider what I believe is the most important of these adaptations, namely how to talk to people about their dementia. This is not to say that all psychotherapeutic work must involve a dialogue around dementia. Instead, it is important for therapists to carry out a thorough assessment of the person's capacity to enter into such a dialogue, considering not only the type and severity of their cognitive impairment, but also their social and personal fragility – issues that I will explore in more depth in Part 4.

Consequently, while I am not suggesting that therapists should always find ways to talk about dementia with their clients, I do believe that therapists should always consider whether to do so. The presumption, then, should be that therapists should start from a position that they will find a way to talk about some aspects of dementia with their client unless there are good indications that this would not be useful. Indeed, it seems to me that this is the only viable ethical position to take (Hughes and Cheston, 2021) – and that it is no more defensible to take a general position that we should not talk about dementia with our clients than it is to imagine that it would be acceptable for a psychotherapist to work with clients with cancer and yet never to speak about this, or to work with someone who was paralysed and not to mention their disability. However, if, after careful consideration, a therapist decides that their client is not capable of engaging with their dementia because of either their cognitive impairment or a precarious social network or a pre-morbid personality that is characterized by narcissistic tendencies, then it may well be that confronting dementia directly is unwise.

Mapping changes in how people talk about their dementia

My first sustained period of trying to use psychotherapy with people who were living with dementia came in the late 1990s when along with Jane Gilliard and Kerry Jones I led a series of short-term psychotherapy groups as part of the Dementia Voice Psychotherapy project (Cheston et al., 2003). The aim of these groups was to provide participants with a space to discuss what it was like for them when their memory was not as good as it used to be. I deliberately left the aim of the sessions open because I did not want to confront participants with their illness at too early a stage – instead I hoped that they would be able to find their own way to the topic of dementia over the course of the sessions. If, however, the group found it too difficult to talk about their dementia, then along with my co-therapists my role was to gradually bring this reluctance into the session so that it could be discussed.

Many participants began the 10-week groups either by insisting that they did not have dementia at all or by minimizing the extent to which it impacted on their lives. While other participants might acknowledge that they had dementia, most were reluctant to share much about their lives or talk with any great emotion about their dementia. However, over the course of the groups, it was striking that the way in which most of the participants talked about what was wrong with them changed. By the end of the 10-week course there was much more openness in the groups about dementia. For some participants, this took the form of acknowledging that they would not get better and having their grief supported in the group. For others, it meant engaging in a more personally relevant and emotional way with their dementia – for instance by moving from an angry rejection to describing what it was about the dementia that most upset them. And on at least one occasion, a participant who had previously been explicit that there was nothing wrong with him began to openly describe himself as having dementia (see Chapter 8). However, not everybody who came to the groups changed – a few left the group at an early point, while others talked (or did not talk) about their dementia in precisely the same way at the end as they had done at the start.

The process of change was also highly variable – over the course of a 90-minute meeting, the atmosphere in the groups oscillated between tears and laughter, with the discussion moving towards and then away from the subject of dementia. After each session, my co-facilitators and I would try to make sense out of what had happened in the session, and about how the way in which people in the group were talking about their dementia was changing. But we had a problem – we did not have a conceptual way to make sense out of these changes in how people were talking, and as a consequence it was hard to record what was taking place, to track change or to note its absence. What we needed was some way to represent this process of change – one that placed the changes that we had seen into a framework. It seemed to me that such a framework would need to encapsulate five key aspects of the changes we were observing.

Firstly, we needed to have a model of change that was sensitive to subtle changes in the way in which people talked about the problems they experienced. While this may seem an obvious point, most researchers at that time talked about people in terms of a binary model in which people either had insight or were in denial about dementia. The reality that we witnessed was one in which participants showed a fluctuating relationship with their illness, with fluid degrees of separation and incorporation.

Secondly, the model needed to reflect the way in which participants talked about dementia as an expression not just of what they were thinking, but also of how they were feeling. Again, this may seem an obvious point, but most of the research that existed at that time represented insight in terms of what the person thought, which in turn was related to the person's neurological functioning. Yet, for us as facilitators, talking about dementia was an inherently emotional process – how people talked about what was happening to them was intimately related to their fears and uncertainties, their losses and their shame.

Thirdly, we were aware that participants in our groups responded to each other and to us as facilitators – in this sense the talk about dementia was social and reactive. The better we became as facilitators in talking about dementia to the group, the more individual group members were able to explore what was happening. Groups seemed to work best when we, as facilitators, said the least, and when the group participants talked to and responded to each other – when they debated and argued over what was happening to them, and when they consoled and supported each other. Our role as facilitators was akin to that of a friendly editor – occasionally intruding to help participants develop their narrative or to gently smooth out inconsistencies (Hoffman, 2001).

Fourthly, the way in which group participants talked about their dementia was labile and fluid, with participants sometimes expressing almost contradictory sentiments about their dementia within a short space of time. It was as if participants were in two or more minds about what, if anything, was wrong with them. This would be seen most obviously when participants talked about their mixed feelings around dementia – for instance, wanting to keep going, but being frightened of what might happen to them or believing that they needed to be strong, but inside feeling as if they were going mad. At times, the conversation between group members seemed to reflect something of an internal debate that was happening for participants.

Finally, we needed to have a methodology to allow us to keep track of the changes that were occurring in the talk across our sessions. Only by charting these changes would we learn how to intervene more effectively, both in terms of doing more of the things that led to change and also to avoid behaving in ways that interfered with the change that was occurring.

The framework that seemed to me to best meet all of these considerations was the Assimilation of Problematic Experiences Scale – a model of change that evolved from psychotherapy process research (Stiles et al., 1999, 1992). However, in order to understand how a model of how people assimilate the problematic aspects of their experiences into their identity can provide a template for adjustment to dementia, we first need to understand why dementia represents a psychological problem.

What is the problem with dementia?

One of the most frequent workshop exercises that I use when I am training staff to work psychotherapeutically with people with dementia is to ask a simple question: 'What would you find the most upsetting aspect of having dementia if you were to be diagnosed with this illness?'. Often this seems to be a question that throws people to some extent – some in the audience take a while to think about it, yet for others the answers are immediate and powerful. Unsurprisingly, what clinicians tell me they dread most parallels what people who actually have dementia have told me in therapy. After all, we are all human – we all share the same fears. Broadly speaking these fears fall into five, overlapping concerns:

1 *Death and deterioration*

None of the many different causes of dementia can be cured, yet all are progressive. One man I worked with described being told that he had Alzheimer's disease as the equivalent of being given a death sentence. At the same time, while we know that people's condition will deteriorate, it's hard to give more than a general indication of how fast or slow this will be – so there is still some uncertainty about the future. Sometimes people in therapy talk in a visceral way about their dread at the thought of what they might become – for instance if they were to become incontinent, with soiled pads perhaps being visible, hearing them rustle under their clothes and perhaps needing to have their most intimate areas washed by a stranger. For others the thing they dread most would be an amplification of their current difficulties – the loss of competence inherent in fumbling over their change at a shop checkout and keeping people waiting, or when they are eating in public and spill their meal because their hands are shaking. As one woman told me (see Chapter 9) what frightened her most was not just the thought of dying but becoming completely useless before this.

2 *Loss of independence and control*

For many people, the hardest thing to face is being dependent on others – including being a burden on the people that they love the most. People fear losing control over so many aspects of their life, from deciding what to wear, to organizing their finances and driving. The prospect of dependency evokes powerful emotions, such as frustration, guilt and shame while the powerlessness that accompanies this typically provokes anxiety and resentment.

3 *Loss of identity*

The thought of becoming someone different – someone unrecognizable to ourselves – is terrifying. Some workshop participants without dementia identify their fear around losing their memories with a fear that they will be changed utterly. Others fear that losing their ability to talk will mean that they lose control over how they look and thus will not be able to decide what version of themselves they present to the world. This too amounts to a change in their identity and one workshop participant recounted graphically that her worst fear was that a paid carer who did not know her would be making assumptions about how she wanted her hair and make-up to be styled. These fears echo Susan Behuniak's (2011) contention that social stereotypes often represent people with dementia as zombies – people who are dead even when they are still alive. For some people living with dementia too, their biggest fear is about how they will be changed, reduced to a person who cannot control themselves. As one man told me, his fear was that he would become like his 'much loved' uncle – previously a quiet and peaceable man who was transformed by dementia into a being who was capable of furious violence against his family and who could not be reasoned with.

4 *Changing relationships with others*

The neurological deterioration caused by different forms of dementia can result in a person losing the ability to recognize others, including the people closest to them. In this, and indeed in many other ways, so dementia directly challenges our ability to be close to others, potentially aggravating feelings of loneliness, isolation and abandonment. As the Dutch psycho-gerontologist Bère Miesen (2016) has pointed out, these changes in cognitive functioning trigger a range of attachment-seeking behaviours, from shadowing carers to parent fixation – the erroneous belief that one's parents are still alive.

5 *Loss of meaning and purpose*

Dementia threatens the loss or transformation of many of the essential building blocks of our identity including the roles we play, our independence and autonomy. Stripped of these fundamental aspects of self, many people with dementia can come to feel that they are neither valued nor useful and that without their former sense of purpose life itself has consequently lost much of its meaning. On several occasions, workshop participants have described how they would cope with dementia by 'going to Zurich' – a euphemism for assisted suicide.

What is clear from participants' responses to these workshop exercises is that not only is the prospect of having dementia terrifying, but that there are so many different ways in which each of us can be terrified – that dementia would bring to each of us our own private horror. For some people the worst aspect might be around being incontinent and fearing the loss of their dignity and humanity. For others the most terrifying prospect would be to lose the security of one's home. For each of us, dementia embodies some of our deepest fears. For each of us there will be a different 'problem' of dementia with which we will need to be reconciled.

The assimilation of psychotherapeutic change model

Psychotherapy process research is a form of qualitative research that focuses on those factors that facilitate (or inhibit) the occurrence of therapeutically significant events within psychotherapy. Before researchers can establish whether change has occurred and, if so, what therapists can do to encourage this, the first thing they need to do is to establish what change involves – that is how people change within psychotherapy. Importantly, psychotherapy process researchers assume that it is possible to identify a common process of change that occurs regardless of what type of therapy is being delivered. In other words, they believe that the process of change is essentially the same whether someone is in psychoanalytic therapy or person-centred counselling or working with a cognitive therapist.

The assimilation of psychotherapeutic change model was developed by a research team, led by Professor Bill Stiles (e.g., Honos-Webb et al., 1999; Osatuke and Stiles, 2006; Stiles, 2001; Stiles et al., 1999, 1992). The assimilation model is not a description of how to do therapy, but rather it provides a way of formulating the way in which people process difficult, emotionally challenging material – in other words, how people's emotions change. The assimilation model has been used to analyse the process of change within psychotherapy with clients experiencing very different challenges including post-traumatic stress (Varvin and Stiles, 1999), bereavement (Wilson, 2011; Wilson et al., 2021) and Arab migrants mourning their lost native culture (Henry et al., 2005, 2009). Among the different case studies that have been explored in depth are Jon Jones, a young man acknowledging his homosexuality (Stiles et al., 1992), Lisa, whose chronic depression stemmed from being mistreated by her husband (Honos-Webb et al., 1998), and Fatima whose daughter had been killed in the midst of terror and torture by a repressive political power (Varvin and Stiles, 1999). The assimilation model has also been used to analyse the process of therapy with people with learning disabilities (Newman and Beail, 2002). Together with a number of different colleagues, I have used it to look at the changes that can occur in how people talk about their dementia in psychotherapy groups (Watkins et al., 2006), in the LivDem course (Cheston et al., 2017) and in conversations between couples (Lishman et al., 2016; Snow et al., 2015).

The assimilation model represents the self not as a single, unified entity but rather as a community of context-dependent, shifting and multiple selves or '*voices*' (Hermans et al., 1992; Mair, 2013; Gergen and Kaye, 1992). The central idea within the assimilation model is that while most experiences in a person's life are unproblematic and can be assimilated routinely into that person's existing understanding of the world, some experiences are so traumatic, and their implications are so threatening that they cannot be easily assimilated into the person's sense of self. When this happens, then a conflict arises between different aspects of the person's self – often between a part of the self that Stiles refers to as the '*dominant voice*' (the voice of continuity, or the preservation of the status quo) and a part of the self that he characterizes as the '*problematic voice*' (which articulates the existence of threats to the established or dominant community of self-voices). In these cases, the conflict that arises between the *problematic* and *dominant voices* prevents the assimilation of the traumatic material, so that it remains unassimilated or unacknowledged – in Stiles' terms 'warded off' (Honos-Webb and Stiles, 1998; Stiles, 2001).

For someone living with dementia, these two voices can be seen in the dilemma that people face in deciding whether or not to talk about their dementia. Often, there is a part of them – a voice – that knows there is something amiss. Perhaps they are aware that they are struggling to remember names or to maintain a conversation. This is a *problematic voice* as it articulates an uncomfortable thought that there may be something wrong. At the same time, there may be another part of them that feels they must not give in by acknowledging their fears and that they should instead press on. This part of the person is the *dominant voice* – it represents the language of the status quo.

The role of psychotherapy, for Stiles, is to facilitate a conversation between the *problematic* and *dominant voices* (Honos-Webb and Stiles, 1998). If the differences between the two voices can be resolved, then this enables the person to engage with, and to integrate, the otherwise unassimilated material into their self. So, for example, a person who is worried whether they might have dementia or not may resolve the difference between their *problematic* and *dominant voice*s by concluding that, although it may be a difficult process, it is better to know if something is wrong and then to face it. Often the process of resolution takes the form of a therapeutic conversation in which the person repeatedly approaches and then retreats from the threatening material – a process that has been described as '*oscillating ambivalence*' (Robinson et al., 2005) and which we have repeatedly encountered in therapeutic work with people living with dementia (e.g., Betts and Cheston, 2011; Cheston et al., 2017; Snow et al., 2015).

While the assimilation model has eight stages, I have found it helpful to simplify movement across these as involving three broad therapeutic tasks: putting a name to dementia but without being overwhelmed; finding distance and perspective; and working through (Cheston, 2013). In the next three chapters I will examine each of these tasks in turn and will suggest that adjustment to dementia involves a continuing, oscillating conversation between a part of the self that engages with the problematic nature of the dementia and another part of the self that resists this.

Final words

People living with dementia are, like us all, semiotic beings – that is to say they seek to make sense out of their lives and what happens to them (Sabat, 2002, 2018). We can assume, then, that people will try to make sense out of the existential reality of their dementia. In order to understand how this might happen, I have drawn on the Assimilation of Problematic Experiences model. This process of adjustment involves the person becoming more at ease with their dementia – they are less frightened by it, and more accepting of it. People change not only how they think about their dementia, but how they feel about it as well. Their relationship with their dementia, in effect, changes. This seems to me to be analogous to other transitions in life and it is tempting therefore to use other ways to describe this: people seem to be '*coming to terms with*' or '*coming out of the closet*' with their dementia (Watkins et al., 2006). In therapeutic terms, so the person needs to make sense of their experience and come to a position where they can see themselves as neither completely changed as a person, nor absolutely the same. Instead, they are the same but different.

In the next three chapters I will set out how the assimilation model frames this process and how therapists can facilitate a conversation about dementia.

8 Putting a name to dementia

This is the first of three chapters, each of which examines a phase in the assimilation process. In this chapter, I will explore how a therapist can begin to bring dementia into the conversation and find a way to talk to someone about their illness. The central task in this phase is for the person to begin to put a name to their dementia without at the same time being emotionally overwhelmed. In Chapter 9 I will then address how to support someone living with dementia who recognizes their dementia in continuing to explore and to make sense of this. Finally, in Chapter 10 I will outline how to help people to work through their dementia and to find partial solutions or *'fixes'* to the problems that they are experiencing.

Emergence

Some years ago, during my training as a clinical psychologist our lecturer gave our class a rule of thumb note as to how to make a differential diagnosis between someone with early dementia and someone who was depressed: both patients would be liable to score badly in a test of cognitive functioning, but there was an important difference. The depressed patient, our lecturer maintained, would complain about their memory and their general cognitive abilities – they would say that their memory was worse now than ever before. A person with dementia, on the other hand, would almost always tell you that their memory was fine, that they did not have any problems in life, and that they were cognitively in as good a state now as they ever had been. The person's level of insight, in other words, was a reliable indication of their clinical condition – our lecturer took it as axiomatic that a person living with dementia would lack awareness about their cognitive functioning.

There are, of course, many elements to the cognitive impairments caused by dementia that impinge on a person's ability to be able to reflect on what has happened to them – to have awareness about their condition, or insight into its causes. The neurological deficits associated with damage to the frontal lobes of the brain that are typical of behavioural-variant frontotemporal dementia (or bv-FTD), in particular, are associated with profound changes in how a person understands and responds to the world. As a result, people whose neuropsychological profile suggests the presence of pre-frontal cortex degeneration or atrophy are likely to experience a range of behavioural and personality changes, including their ability to place themselves into the shoes of others, or to understand the world from that person's point of view. Lacking this capacity to understand how others see them, many people with bv-FTD, or other forms of frontal lobe damage, are no longer able to see themselves as having changed – an issue that I will return to in Chapter 11.

However, Frontotemporal Dementia including the behavioural variant are, thankfully, rare. While other forms of dementia, including Alzheimer's disease, do involve damage to the same areas of the brain, especially in the later stages, many people living with dementia do not fit into the stereotype of dementia that was prevalent when I trained. In the last few years, people like Kate Swaffer, Keith Oliver, Wendy Mitchell, Norman McNamara, Christine Bryden and many others, all of whom are living with dementia, have written about their experiences and have been powerful advocates for the rights of people living with dementia (e.g., Bryden, 2005; Oliver, 2019; Swaffer, 2016). Collectively this advocacy has been a powerful force for change and indicates the essential fallacy of supposing that the cognitive impairments underlying their conditions will inevitably prevent someone from talking about their dementia.

Indeed, there is evidence that even people with severe levels of cognitive impairment can still think and talk about what is happening to them, even to the point of being able to think about their own death (Goodwin and Waters, 2009). Other evidence also points to at least some people living with dementia continuing to be aware of what is happening to them, even though their dementia has worsened. In one quantitative study, almost 200 people with dementia were followed over a period of 18 months to chart the relationship between their awareness of dementia and other aspects of their life (Aalten et al., 2006). While the level of awareness of participants generally worsened during the study, around a fifth of patients who were rated as having an intact level of awareness at baseline continued to have this 18 months later on. In addition, another three participants showed an improvement in levels of awareness over the course of the study. Similarly, in the IDEAL study, the majority of the 83 participants with dementia who were rated as having low awareness at the start of the study gained awareness over the course of the study, some as late as four or more years after their initial diagnosis (Alexander et al., 2022).

There is good reason, then, to conclude that with a few exceptions, a person's apparent awareness of their dementia, or lack of awareness, is rarely simply a result of neurological damage. Instead, their capacity to make sense of the many different threats posed by their dementia will also vary according to their psychological resources, and the type of threat to their identity that they are presented with. For some people, it is well within their capability to be consistently clear about their dementia and to address the issues as they arise. Yet for others, this is more difficult, and they tend to avoid engaging with their dementia. In these cases where someone's attention is drawn to their dementia (as I set out in Chapter 3), this sets off a series of defences that protect the self against threat and thus prevents this threat from destabilizing their psychological equilibrium. However, when we augment a person's psychological resources, including their levels of self-esteem, then these reminders of dementia are experienced as less of a threat, and their need for psychological defences will be reduced (Cheston et al., 2015).

In describing the psychological processes that underpin assimilation I have slightly adapted the model outlined by Stiles and his colleagues. Thus, the eight original levels of Stiles will be grouped in terms of three tasks: firstly, helping dementia to emerge as the problem without the person being emotionally overwhelmed; secondly, gaining emotional distance and perspective; and finally, trying out partial solutions to problems.

In Chapters 9 and 10 I will address the therapeutic work that is possible when a person has begun to talk about their dementia and needs to find some emotional distance from it and to identify practical ways of living with it. In the current chapter, however, I will briefly describe how the three initial levels from Stiles' eight-stage model (warding off awareness, unwanted voices and vague awareness) can be considered as comprising a single stage of emergence. The task for a therapist working with a client with dementia who is at this stage is to begin to have a conversation with the person about what is wrong – something that I refer to as 'bringing dementia into the room' – and it is often a slow process in which the therapist assesses the person's capacity and willingness to engage with their dementia. Where the person's self is so fragile that they cannot tolerate the threat to self that dementia represents, it will often be wise to decide not to continue to engage them in talking about dementia. I will return to this subject in Chapter 12 where I consider working with personal and social fragility.

Table 8.1 summarizes this stage of emergence, breaking this down into Stiles's original three levels as well as setting out the key therapeutic tasks for clients and therapists and the types of intervention that might help in this work.

The assimilation model: From warding off to vague awareness

Level 0: Warding off

The first stage of the assimilation model is one in which material that is problematic for the self is almost completely pushed away or, to use Stiles's terms 'warded off'. Often, when I worked with someone who was living with dementia, they would tell me that while they might have a physical disability such as loss of mobility, or a sensory impairment such as poor eyesight or loss of hearing, they did not have any cognitive difficulties at all. These clients refused to acknowledge that they experienced any difficulties in their daily life as a result of cognitive changes. Instead, they either entirely avoided these issues or blamed problems that they encountered on other causes, such as a problem with their hearing or a misunderstanding. Many people whose way of talking (or not talking) about their cognitive problems fell into this level showed little outward sign of distress about what was happening to them, although at the same time they were often rather suspicious of what I, or my colleagues, wanted and often blamed their family or friends intensely for making problems for them.

As a psychologist providing a psychotherapeutic service within memory services, I was often asked to meet people who were struggling with the diagnosis of Alzheimer's disease or another form of dementia. Occasionally, this

Table 8.1 Therapeutic tasks and strategies at the different assimilation levels during the emergence phase

Assimilation level	Behaviour and affect	Therapeutic task of client	Therapeutic task of therapist	Possible interventions
0. Warding off	Successful avoidance, non-engagement, problems located in physical or sensory changes, or due to ageing. Affect is minimal.	To begin to notice and to think about problems.	To create a safe place for the person with dementia to begin to explore their experiences.	Need to be cautious and adopt an ethical approach to informal engagement. Talk about change in a general way (e.g., growing older) to assess capacity to change. Where the person seems unable to explore dementia, then consider working with family carer.
1. Unwanted thoughts	The *problematic voice* is located in others. Attachment-seeking behaviour. Client may be frightened of losing control. May externalize the dementia or use stories as metaphors to explore emotions associated with dementia. Affect is unfocused, includes intrusion of strong emotions and shame.	To begin to hear the *problematic voice* directly (without being overwhelmed by distress).	To hold onto both the *problematic* and *dominant* voices within the therapeutic space.	Notice dementia-related experiences without making causal judgements, e.g., lapses and signs of covering up. Introduce indirect ways of addressing dementia-related experiences (e.g., use narratives and third-person explorations). Consider teaching stress reduction techniques (e.g., relaxation, mindfulness).
2. Vague awareness	Client alternates between approaching and avoiding dementia-related experiences. Checking for slips. Indirect expression of *problematic voice*. Distress is the hallmark of this level and begins to centre around dementia-related experiences.	To begin to articulate problematic experiences and acknowledge emotional reactions to these.	To help the client to place some form on their expressions of problematic material, while containing associated anxiety.	Ensure therapeutic work is predictable and with secure boundaries. Pick up on expressions of anxiety or distress, including fears of losing control. Tentatively introduce names for these fears. Hold onto articulation of emotion-related material. Help the client to step back from their emotions, and to begin to talk about their reaction to dementia. Ensure that client has clear feedback about the diagnosis. Mobilize and address external resources (e.g., attend to family dynamics).

struggle took the form of the person rejecting their diagnosis or refusing to acknowledge it in some way. When I subsequently met the client, in order for me to understand whether I would be able to have a conversation with them about their dementia, I tried to assess the extent to which they were able to notice and to think about problems in their lives. The capacity of allowing one-self to be changed in some way is essential if the person is to be helped to engage with their dementia and to vocalize any part of their experience as problematic. Within the assimilation model, the initial therapeutic task for a client, then, is to notice and to think about the problematic aspects of their life. The task for the therapist is to create a safe place for this to happen – and to assess from the responses of the client whether they have the capacity to engage in the work of thinking about change.

In talking to people who were warding off their dementia, I would often start by talking in broad terms about ageing and the changes, differences and indeed benefits that this can bring. As well as helping to build the person's life history, this also enabled me to gauge their emotional resilience by assessing the ver-sion of themselves that they created: was this a story in which they were the hero of their own narrative, perhaps thwarted in their aims by others? Or was it a more nuanced version of life in which they might be open to thinking about having changed themselves? To this end, I would ask about any sensory or physical impairments that the person had and would try to understand how the disability that these changes brought had been accommodated. Finally, I would also ask about their memory, perhaps by addressing this in the third person through a question such as: '*Often people notice as they grow older that their memory for what has recently happened to them gets slowly worse – is this something that you've been aware of?*'. Importantly, I tried to steer away from suggesting at this point that a person's difficulties were more than could be considered the norm for someone of their age.

Where the person was warding off their dementia entirely, then they would not take up any invitation to acknowledge any lapse in their self-competencies and would instead attribute any impairment of functioning to external causes. The conversation about change could become difficult to sustain, and it could feel uncomfortable to continue with this line of conversation. There was also an additional tension in working with people who ward off their dementia: it was only possible to have a conversation about dementia within the context of a therapeutic relationship, which takes time and patience to build. However, when the existence of the problem is being pushed away, the person does not, themselves, experience that there is a problem to be worked with and there is no agreed basis for therapy to proceed. Individual therapy is, therefore, not possible. At the same time, the pushed-away problems do not disappear – instead they become problems for others to deal with. For people who are liv-ing with dementia these problems are typically picked up and responded to by the person's partner or carer: it is they who have to live with the gulf between life-as-it-is and the person's life-as-I-would-have-it. It is the family carer who needs to act as the memory for the person who will not acknowledge that they forget and who will likely as not receive no thanks for this. In these instances, where the individual with dementia themselves will not engage in therapeutic work, then often the only remaining therapeutic option is to support the person's carer separately from the person with dementia.

My experience of trying to talk to clients about their dementia was that comparatively few people consistently warded off their dementia. Instead, the large majority of people who were referred to me were able, to at least some extent, to enter into a conversation about something being wrong – even if for many it was too difficult to put a name to this change. It is to this group of people for whom the problematic experience of dementia is beginning to emerge into dialogue that I will now turn.

Level 1: Unwanted voices

Whereas in the warding off level of assimilation the *problematic voice* is silent, in the next level, the emotionally charged aspect of the person's dementia begins to become apparent. Consequently, what emerges is the beginning of a dialogue between the *problematic voice*, which often takes the form of a relatively unformed insistence that something is wrong, and a reactive, *dominant voice* that seeks to minimize or dismiss its relevance. Consequently, the emotional distress associated with acknowledging the existence of dementia is minimized.

We can see the emergence of the *problematic voice* as the person with dementia acknowledges that something is wrong in their life but refers to this indirectly – for instance as *'the problem'* or *'it'*. The problem of dementia is recognized, then, but not named. Instead, the articulation of the *problematic voice* relating to dementia calls forth another voice, as the person who is living with dementia maintains that they should be able to cope, for instance by using phrases such as needing to *'tough it out'* or to *'soldier on'*. The emphasis in the person's discourse is on controlling or suppressing this frightening emotional material. Often it is the therapist, and not the client, who initiates the discussion of change, with the client's acknowledgement followed by their changing the conversation. In this way, the person may shift the topic of conversation away from dementia and on to a more neutral topic. This switching of topic can be seen in this extract from one of the groups in the Dementia Voice group therapy project that Becky Watkins and I analysed. In this extract Ms G interrupts the conversation between another participant and the facilitator, and in making a joke shifts the conversation away from a potentially difficult issue (Watkins, 2006):

Facilitator: *Are there some things, are there some things that you can't laugh at?*

Mr J: *I suppose there are [Long pause]*

Ms G: *We should be laughing then! [The group bursts out laughing]*

The fear of losing control

When someone who is working at the level of unwanted voices is unable to move away from the distress that thoughts of their dementia provoke, then the subsequent rise in affect represents an unbalancing of emotional equilibrium. For many, the emergence of strong feelings can itself be distressing – the person may feel that they have lost control of their emotions. At this point in therapy, people often tell me that they fear that they are going mad, or somehow losing a battle to control themselves. Often, they describe having to make a choice between continuing to engage with their dementia at the risk of losing control, or to back away from these types of reminders and to avoid further engagement. The following exchange from the same Dementia Voice group illustrates the way in which another participant, Mr E, found himself facing just such a dilemma. During his pre-therapy meetings with my co-facilitator, Mr E had recognized that his memory was deteriorating, which he found upsetting. He was then offered group therapy. At the start of the first session of the group Mr E struggled to put into words the conflict between his awareness of something being wrong (the *problematic voice*) and his urge not to think about it and risk losing control (the *dominant voice*):

Mr E: *I find what we're doing now, it brings all memories to me, so and being around listening to you all, talking. I find I just want to be [pause]*

Facilitator: *Normal?*

Mr E: *Well not normal, no. I don't think a memory loss and I don't. Talking, and being around each other. I'm not being funny about that. I'm trying to make a point that I'd rather be at home doing what I need to do and want to do and this is why I really don't want to talk about that you know. I mean I'm sure it's being selfish but it's just the way I feel about it. I don't really want to be here.*

Facilitator: *Sometimes the things you remember that are the most painful and you do want to forget about it all.*

Mr E: *Yes, that's exactly, yes that's exactly what it is.*

Mrs A: *Does it disturb you, that you can't or does it—*

Mr B: *Depress you?*

Mr E: *Well, I just don't want to be here. I just want to be. I've got lots of things I'd like to do, and er. Well, I can't think about coming here, it just brings it all back.*

At this, my co-facilitator intervened to say that she felt Mr E was saying that he would like to leave the group. He agreed that he was, and she arranged for a taxi to be called to take him home. For Mr E thinking about memory dysfunction seems to have risked destabilizing his psychological equilibrium and he articulated a clear choice between either staying in the group and risking the emotional consequences of engaging with his dementia, or leaving and continuing to ward off the distress associated with the illness. It is important to note that despite the therapy session being held within the local branch of the

Alzheimer Society with the name of the charity being written in large letters over the front door, nevertheless Mr E did not use the terms '*dementia*' or '*Alzheimer's disease*'. Instead, he restricted himself to using the more neutral term '*memory loss*' – quite possibly because if he had named his dementia directly then this would have risked provoking further distress.

Externalising dementia

Another way in which people living with dementia sometimes try to reduce the distress that arises from dementia is to externalize this as a problem that belongs to others. Thus, in the group session following Mr E's departure, Mr B mentioned dementia for the first time:

> Mr B: *Well, there are two business clubs in [name of town where he lives] and they are very good, because everyone is in the same age bracket and half of them have got Alzheimer's or something near, so we've all worked out ways of reminding each other in the conversation. You don't just stand there and say something, you lead into it, so people know what they are doing.*

In a similar way, the existence of dementia can be both acknowledged yet also located outside the person by using the pronoun 'you'. Thus Len (Lishman et al., 2016) switched between talking about himself in the first and second person. At the end of the research interview the researcher, Emma Lishman, asked Len to look back at his initial fears about receiving a diagnosis at the memory clinic and what he would advise someone else in his position to do:

> Len: *I think that if people know, they understand, but if you hide it as I did, first going, they get frustrated with you. So, if I was advising someone, if they found themselves in the situation I found myself in, I think you've got to be open with people and they may understand instead of thinking, 'Oh that silly old fool is losing his marbles' ... I mean I tried to cover up, which I suppose is a natural thing to do. Yeah, you try to cover up and swear blind that you haven't been told, you know, what you have been told, and eventually you accept the reality that you're not right. And I think that took a long time for me to recognize it, but I'm glad that it happened, you know. I'm glad that it was brought to people's attention.*
> (Lishman et al., 2016)

Storytelling as a metaphor for dementia

In order to reduce distress, people working at this level may refer to dementia indirectly, for instance by using euphemisms such as memory loss rather than a diagnostic term. At times, people with dementia may also describe their dementia or their response to their dementia through metaphors. Thus, Henry, a second participant that Emma Lishman interviewed, replied to her enquiry around his worries of attending a memory clinic by using the analogy of a soldier contemplating surrendering to an enemy:

Emma: *Is that [memory dysfunction] something you have worried about since coming back from the memory clinic?*

Henry: *It [memory dysfunction] has been in my mind, yes, erm, because in a way it's almost writing you off and I don't think that is right at all, but you are suddenly becoming somebody totally different to what you used to be and mentally you don't want that. Mentally you don't want to accept that, and I think that's a good thing. Because once you start waving the white flag, you pack up and I don't want that ... Well I think, you have got to have a positive attitude in life. If you don't, you just wave the white flag and you pack it all in, and I don't want that, no ... I mean once you have reached the age of 80, it's ever so easy to wave the white flag and say, 'Oh, I can't do this, I can't do that,' but you have got to have a positive attitude, which I think I have got.*

(Lishman et al., 2016)

For Henry, acknowledging his dementia seems to be experienced as being akin to surrendering. However, while he uses the term '*waving the white flag*' three times, at no point does he ever describe who or what he is fighting against. His enemy remains invisible. An extension of this defensive strategy occurs when people with dementia describe aspects of their dementia but relate this to other aspects of their lives. This tendency can be seen most vividly in some of the stories that people may recount. While ostensibly about another part of their life, often from many years previously, sometimes it is possible to glimpse emotional themes that bear upon aspects of the life that the person is living today.

The storytelling that can take place in working with older people living with dementia fits into the established tradition within psychotherapy of viewing the stories that clients tell in relation to emerging therapeutic themes. These stories, so it is argued, can act as symbolic expressions of the problematic material – allowing it to be explored, but also providing some distance from that material, thereby limiting the amount of psychological pain that would be experienced. For instance, in *The Uses of Enchantment* (1976), Bettelheim suggested that traditional fairy tales, with themes such as abandonment, death, and injury allowed children to grapple with their fears in remote, symbolic terms. Reading and interpreting these fairy tales, so Bettelheim believed, would provide children with a sense of meaning and emotional growth that would better prepare them for their own futures.

I believe that we can view the stories that people with dementia tell in a similar way. Often, these stories seem to me to carry rich, symbolic meanings that can act as metaphorical workings through or explorations of significant issues that cannot be addressed directly as they are potentially too emotionally overwhelming. Under certain circumstances, this process of metaphorical exploration can aid the assimilation of problematic experiences and thus be therapeutic. One example of this can be seen in the stories told by Roy – a member of one of the first psychotherapy groups that I led (Cheston, 1996).

Roy: Dementia as a jungle

Roy was a 74-year-old man who had a diagnosis of Alzheimer's disease and who had recently moved into the area as his family felt he could no longer care for himself. Instead, he was now being cared for by his stepdaughter, who had organized for him to have regular stays in respite care. Roy was one of seven people attending a group that I facilitated at a day hospital, the aim of which was to allow people to talk about how life was for them. Roy had missed the previous session of the group, as he had been staying for a week in a nursing home, and he had come straight to the day hospital from that home, with his suitcase packed, ready to return to live at his stepdaughter's home that afternoon.

During the session, Roy described how life sometimes seems to go in a cycle, and that he could draw on his past experiences to help him to manage new situations, thinking to himself, 'Oh, I've done this before'. Louise, my co-facilitator, asked him if he could think of a situation like this. Roy replied:

'Yes, there was a case. There was an example in Malaya. We had a job to do, and we couldn't do it because of the situation of the country – the difficulty of getting through the jungle, thick jungle, high grass and things like that. And I spotted somebody nearby, and he was talking to somebody else, and I went up to him and in fact he was talking about his airplane and what he was going to do at that particular time and so I went up to him and said, "Do you want a pilot?" and he said "yes" and that was it, although I didn't realize it at the time.

And in fact, I assisted in several situations where he had to fly the aircraft out of awkward situations and land it somewhere else where it was difficult to get out again. So, I put him right on things like that. And I had it organized for a clearing of the jungle path where you were going to land and where we were already fixed at the time to make it safe, to at least making the whole area safe, to at least making the whole area safe for getting in and out of quickly. And the jungle of course grew while we were there to the point that we used oil and petrol and therefore we cleared it, and it came in very useful. And I was busy on that for about a year and a half approximately. It was one aircraft and it never let me down I must admit.'

On a first reading this may seem like a straightforward account of an episode from Roy's past life as a pilot. Certainly, telling the story may serve a function of enhancing Roy's identity within the group: by recounting a time when he was playing an important and valued role as part of a larger enterprise, so this story is likely to boost Roy's self-esteem and enhance his feeling of being connected to others – psychological resources that I argued in Chapter 2 can buffer people against existential threat.

There is also a possibility that telling this story has another function for Roy. According to Roy's explanation, the point of him telling the story is that it illustrates how past experiences help him to manage present-day problems. Yet, it is less clear exactly how the story might help him in this way – how there might be a link between recalling this story and his present life. Nevertheless, when Roy is then pushed to explain this, so he continues to maintain that '*situations that you get into often are very similar to those situations that occurred in Malaya*'. At the same time, Roy also knows that '*at the moment, light aircraft of the type that you fly, they're not very similar*'. So, in what way can it be the case that remembering stories like this from his past helped Roy in the present? Well, one possibility might be that there was indeed something about Roy's time flying a plane in the jungles of Malaya, carving landing strips out of the jungle, only to find them regrow and needing to be burnt out again, that connects with his experiences of dementia.

Right at the start of his story, Roy prefaces it by remembering that there was a time when '*we had a job to do, and we couldn't do it because of the situation of the country*'. It may be that this is the similarity to Roy's present life – that once again he has a job to do but cannot do it because of the situation. If we allow the possibility that Roy's current job is to get on with the business of his life, then he is indeed struggling to do this because of his situation. He can no longer live on his own, and instead, he needs to live with his stepdaughter so that she can look after him. However, she cannot do this without having regular breaks, which is why Roy has to stay in the nursing home – somewhere that he struggles to remember. At other times in the group, Roy had described how living with a severely disrupted memory was a day-to-day struggle for him. It may well be, then, that while the story of his time in Malaya as a pilot was not useful to him now in a practical sense, it is nevertheless still useful for him as a metaphor. Indeed, Roy knows that this period in his life is not practically useful as he later says that '*nobody has any airplanes around here*'. More specifically, the story may provide Roy with a way of making sense out of his experience of dementia. The feeling of searching after meaning, only to find it slipping away from him as he grasps it, may feel a little like it did to him when he was in Malaya trying to negotiate a way through thick jungle and high grass that needed to be burnt down, but that kept growing back. By extension, as he managed to find a way to survive in Malaya all those years ago, so he may well find a way to survive now.

In this way, the story of the jungle may, for Roy, have provided an important psychological resource – it may have helped him to find a meaning in life that would otherwise escape him. The story might be useful because it helps him to remember a time in life that is analogous to his current life – and a time of life when he had been a useful, productive and valuable member of a wider group, even though at times it was hard for him to know where he was and whether he would find safety again. The importance of this story might be that it provided him with the reassurance that if he persists, then he can ultimately find a way through.

Working psychotherapeutically with unwanted material

Where a person living with dementia is working at this early level of assimilation, the therapeutic task is to help the client to hold onto the knowledge both that something has changed (the *problematic voice*) and that at their core, they remain the same person (the *dominant voice*) and to do so gradually and in a way that does not overwhelm them. The therapist needs to work with the person's defences, not against them. I will now consider some of the different ways that I have found to do this.

Noticing dementia

In my conversations with people living with dementia, there are frequent instances in which dementia intrudes. This may take the form of cognitive slips in which the person repeats themselves or forgets names, dates or events. At other times, they may try to avoid placing themselves in a position where they may slip – for instance by using generic terms of friendship such as 'mate' or 'pal' rather than a name. Similarly, people with dementia may seek to anticipate or excuse in advance any error they may subsequently make, by talking about how their memory is not so good as it was or referring to having an especially bad day.

There are three possible ways to respond to this. One possibility is to ignore these slips, evasions or attempts at covering up – and indeed this is often a preferred strategy especially in the initial stages of therapy. There is a therapeutic risk, however, that by ignoring the evidence of dementia we miss the opportunity to openly acknowledge the gravity of the situation – and thus communicate the message that there is something that we are both aware of, but which neither of us feels able to talk about. The second possibility is to simply refer to the dementia directly as a potential cause of these errors and coping strategy. While this can be productive, there is a clear risk that this may produce a counter-productive response and push the person into a deeper avoidance. There is a third way – namely to notice these instances but to do so empathically and in a way that allows the person to comment on their behaviour.

So, for instance, it can be helpful to remember a memory slip and to refer back to this later in the therapeutic process. Initially, these comments should be directed at the symptoms of the dementia, rather than the condition itself, and a query around the person's responses to this. This might take the form of a comment such as: *'I've noticed that you seemed unsure as to whether we've met before'*, or *'I know it can be a bit embarrassing to talk about this sort of thing, but I couldn't help noticing that you've asked me three times now about whether I'd like a cup of tea'*. In terms of the assimilation model, reflections like this encompass both the *problematic voice* (the person is making mistakes) and the *dominant voice* (the need to ignore or to push this away).

The objective of bringing the existence of some aspect of dementia into the conversation is not to embarrass or to make someone feel uncomfortable, but merely to try to begin to have a conversation about what it is like for them to have a failing memory – to allow this to be something that can be talked about. At this stage, it may not be appropriate to associate the cognitive slip with a diagnosis. Instead, typically, the conversation can continue to explore the person's responses to their slip – the behavioural strategies that they use, and the emotional payoffs for these. This may take the form of suggesting how the person may experience something of a dilemma in seeking to resolve the tension between their *dominant* and *problematic voices*. Thus, the therapist might eventually offer a tentative reflection to the effect that *'on the one hand it seems you're a bit unsure as to whether anything is wrong – sometimes you seem to make these silly mistakes, and your family is worried about you. But on the other hand, it's really too much to think about, because after all, memory loss is a part of old age'*.

Talking about dementia indirectly

I have described above how a feature of the unwanted voices level of assimilation is that while dementia is referred to, this is done indirectly either through metaphors within stories, or by externalizing the dementia. While we can never be entirely sure that the stories people tell us relate in some way to the emotions that they experience, often by drawing parallels between the two we may be able to help people to process some of their otherwise unrecognized affective responses to dementia. One such example of this attention to storytelling can be seen in the way in which dialogue between two participants, Martin and Andy, changed over the course of a 10-week psychotherapy group (Cheston et al., 2004).

Martin and Andy: Optimism and pessimism

Andy and Martin were members of a therapy group that I established as part of the *Dementia Voice* project. During the first session, Martin insisted that the difficulties he was facing were temporary and that both his skills and also those of other group members would return over the course of the 10 weeks that we were to meet for. Sitting opposite Martin was Andy, who had been diagnosed with a form of dementia that limited his capacity to speak. Andy struggled to compose sentences, but when he did so he told Martin that he did not believe him – his life was changed forever. Martin bristled at this, telling the group angrily that Andy was jealous as he had *'the gift of the gab'*.

During the second session, Martin spoke poignantly (albeit briefly) about how his life has changed, before going on almost immediately to relate a story about his childhood in which he had been walking along a deserted beach when a bi-plane had landed nearby to ask for directions. This abrupt movement away from an articulation of a problematic part of his life is characteristic of the '*unwanted thoughts*' level of the assimilation model. Rather than talk about the present, Martin instead recounted stories from his childhood, including a narrative of looking for freedom among the clouds.

In the early stages of the fourth session of the group, almost all participants described changes in their lives, including difficulties with their memory. Martin briefly referred to having had to give up driving his car. He then went on to recount a series of stories, the longest of these concerned how he and his wife had taken a series of cruises[2].

'*Here's a story for you. I don't know whether you'll believe it, but this is what happened as I'm sitting here right now speaking to you. I was in the bar – we'd just got up – and I looked out of the window and saw this line on the horizon, and there's me, a country bumpkin boy, seeing this and so I turn to my wife and say, "Look at this, darling. You'll never see another one of these in your life."*

'*So, she looks up and says, "What's this?" And I says, "Well, that's a tidal wave and it's coming straight for us." "Well," she said. "Nah, don't be silly." But then in a little while, she looks up and it's still coming our way, so she says, "You're right, you are, that's what it is."*

'*So, I says to the barman that he better get on the phone to the captain and tell him to put up the sides of the funnel, so that the funnel isn't flooded. And he says, "Well, no. You're wrong. You don't get tidal waves where we are." But a bit later on, he said that we were right, that there was a tidal wave coming towards us. And I turned to my wife and my oldest daughter and told them that we needed to get ourselves into the bar so that we would be out of the way. But as we start to go up the wave, I turn to them and say, "How about we go outside now and see what it's like?" And that ship, she went up the wave so that you'd not even notice that anything had happened, and when we went outside, we saw that we had got to the top, and it was like being on the top of a mountain. And then down we went the other side, and that ship, boy were she wonderful, you'd not even noticed that we had moved, that anything had happened to us – 43,000 tons she was, and you'd hardly notice she had moved.*

'*And when we went to bed that night, I turned on the radio and we listened to the BBC news, and it said that the Canberra had been in a tidal wave, but that it had come out of it with nobody on board injured. So, I said to my wife that that's it, there's no doubt about that then. And then it went onto say that the Cunard board had let it be known that on either side of the Canberra in case anything had happened were the Star of India and the Empress, and that that had just docked at Falmouth with 200 people on board.*'

(Cheston et al., 2004)

At the end of this narrative, my co-facilitator asked Martin if there were any parallels with life now. He replied that there were and that 70 per cent of

---

2 Unlike other extracts that I have included in this book, I did not record the sessions in this particular group. Instead, immediately after the group had finished, I made detailed notes of what had been said.

people get through difficult times. She later suggested to Martin that he was concerned for Andy and that he'd like Andy to join in the conversation. Andy raised his head and said to Martin, *'You do, don't you?'* in a warm and supportive way, as if he was glad that Martin was interested in him.

During this session, Martin's narrative began to concern different elements of threat rather than to relate rather idealized accounts of his childhood. In his story of the tidal wave threatening the cruise liner there were a number of strands that reflected the emotional impact of the changes in his life that he occasionally referred to. At first, the story concerns whether the threat that Martin sees is real. Then, when the nature of the threat becomes apparent, so the story develops to consider whether this threat can be survived before finally, when the threat has been negotiated, it becomes apparent on reflection that although support has been there for his ship, others had not been so fortunate.

It is possible that the symbolic expression of the problematic aspects of dementia in this story from his life enabled Martin to explore the emotions associated with his dementia, while also allowing him to distance himself from that material and thereby limiting the amount of psychological pain that he experienced (Stiles et al., 1999). In this case, the main elements of the cruise liner narrative concern threat, and an exploration of the nature of that threat. Yet the story concludes with the threat having been survived.

During the fifth session, the problems that Martin experienced began to be more explicitly defined. He spoke of how forgetting was like *'a steel door coming down on me'* and apologized to others for the weakness in his bladder that meant that he had to go out to the toilet during the group. This fifth session represented an important therapeutic step forward for Martin. In previous sessions, although other participants had spoken of having Alzheimer's disease, or had discussed their memory difficulties, Martin had restricted himself to speaking vaguely of changes in his life without detailing them. In this session, however, he had been able to speak more coherently of a problem with his memory. At the same time, the nature of the problem was not specified and even though he acknowledged that *'things look bad'* Martin still maintained the hope that his problem would be resolved.

In the eighth session, Martin was able for the first time to acknowledge both that the cause of his difficulties had been a stroke and also that he was worried about the future. Not only was the nature of the problem defined, but Martin was able to present some understanding about why the problem existed, and an awareness of what the problem might mean for his future. Some of the thematic elements of Martin's narratives during this session reflected this higher level of assimilation. Thus, he recounted a new story of chickens being attacked both by foxes (who leave them as little more than a carcass) and then being destroyed by storms. Unlike his story of the cruise liner, however, these narratives did not conclude with the threat being survived.

Over the course of the group there had been noticeable tension between the loquacious Martin and the quiet, linguistically impaired Andy. In one sense, the latter had enacted the *problematic voice* of change and resignation to the former's optimistic *dominant voice*. However, not only did their relationship steadily evolve and improve over the course of the group but their positions around dementia also grew closer.

Working indirectly through a proxy

Another technique that can facilitate an indirect exploration of the person's problems is for the therapist to ask the client for advice about understanding what another person may be going through – someone with similar problems to those that the client has experienced. Heather, a trainee clinical psychologist that I supervised used this technique in her work with Sonia and Clive.

Sonia and Clive

Sonia was an 80-year-old woman who had been diagnosed with Alzheimer's disease some years previously and who, when Heather (a trainee psychologist I was supervising) and I first met them, was living at home with her husband Clive. Nine months before this, Sonia had been admitted for 10 weeks to an in-patient assessment ward for people with dementia. The trigger for this admission had been that Sonia had developed a number of delusions, for instance becoming convinced that the house that she lived in for 20 years was not hers, and that Clive was not her husband. Although both seemed very similar to her 'real' house and her 'real' husband, she was sure that if only she searched hard enough, then she could find the genuine ones.

When we met them both, these delusions were still occasionally present for Sonia, but they were now much less distressing for her. However, she had since also developed a habit of setting the dining table for her brothers and father who she was convinced would be coming to stay with her. Clive and Sonia were referred to the psychology team as he was worried that things might get worse for Sonia again. Heather and I initially met Clive on his own and discussed how he understood his wife's behaviour. He told us that he felt that Sonia had experienced some sort of nervous breakdown and explained that while he knew that she got things muddled because of her dementia, what had occurred before her admission felt very different to him. During this period, he felt that Sonia's distress at her neurological impairment had been increasingly apparent – for instance she had started to be distressed if he had to leave her. Together we explored whether Sonia's difficulties might reflect feelings of insecurity and distress (Miesen, 2016). We agreed that Heather would meet Sonia to understand more about how she was coping.

On Sonia's first meeting with Heather, she told her that she had enjoyed her time on the ward even though she had not thought that there was anything wrong with her. Her husband and daughter had felt that she had had a nervous breakdown, but she had felt fine. Sonia then spoke of her belief that she had an enduring soul – an aspect of her being that stayed with her throughout her life, no matter what hardships she faced. Sonia also told Heather that there was an identical house to the one that they were in now and remarked on the strangeness of this. Heather reflected that sometimes things can look different when you are worried – a suggestion that Sonia did not respond to.

In their next session Sonia talked about 'not feeling myself … I don't feel in my own skin' as if there were two people inside her sometimes. Heather remembered Sonia's comments about an enduring soul – still having the same values and ideals that made her uniquely her. Sonia told her, 'That's it exactly,' and talked about how feeling at home was something that grew gradually inside you. At this point Heather asked Sonia for her help in understanding a lady on the ward who was having difficulty adjusting to leaving her home and staying on the ward. Sonia told her that the lady's experience was like a 'ball of wool unravelling'.

The following week Sonia told Heather that her memory was bothering her – that it comes back to her eventually, but that she gets frustrated and cross with herself. She said, 'I'm not potty, I've said it all along'. Heather suggested that although she certainly was not potty, nevertheless something was different with her and that they should spend time trying to make sense out of what had changed. She reminded Sonia of her description of the woman on the ward as unravelling, and Sonia seized on this, saying that this was exactly what she felt too.

The next time that they met, Sonia told Heather that although she had always maintained that there was nothing wrong with her when she was admitted to the ward, she wanted to ask Heather what she thought about cells being lost in the brain and how that affected people, because they obviously do not come back. Heather agreed that once cells are lost, then they cannot come back. She reflected that this could make people feel anxious and frightened. In response, Sonia described a time when she felt she had unravelled: her GP had been called out to see her at her home and had told her that this was the house she had always lived in. Ruefully, she commented that he must think she was potty.

As they continued to work together, so Sonia talked more about the lady on the ward and how she too was beginning to realize that something had changed in her. She described her own experience of a CT scan when she was told that there were bits missing in her brain. She said that it was different to having a broken leg – the mind was different.

On Heather's eighth visit to see Sonia, she found her in an excited and animated state. Sonia explained that 'I feel normal … I've suddenly seen it all … I've not been lying – it's changed up here [tapping her head], and it's telling me that things are different … it was my mind telling me that it was different'. She knew that there were times when she thought she was in the wrong house and that this happened because 'my mind has slipped'. Sonia spoke of how she could not always understand or remember things in the way that she used to do. She spoke of being aware that something would come over her and that for a second or two she felt completely empty – unable to think of anything. At these times she was aware that she wasn't the same person that she used to be, that it was she who had changed, not the world around her. As they discussed this, Sonia told Heather that she now felt very shaken and that she had been mistaken – she asked her, 'Can anything be done?' Heather replied that when brain cells were lost, they could not be replaced, and that therefore it was more about coping with the problem than getting rid of it. Sonia replied tearfully, 'Well, it's the end of my life.'

Over the next few months as Heather and I continued to visit, so Sonia oscillated between two contrasting positions. At times, she became distressed and insisted that she was in the wrong house. When she felt like this, Sonia refused to accept that there was anything wrong with her. At other times Sonia recalled the unravelling which she described as a release, as if she was casting aside a heavy velvet gown. However, this also left her feeling worried that she might forget this insight and that her mind might slip again, as it was difficult to hold onto the reality of how she had changed. She asked whether it was possible for one side of her brain to discipline the other and tell it that what it was seeing was not real.

Level 2: Vague awareness

Coming to terms with dementia is a painful process. The gradual emergence of awareness is a process that is analogous to entering a brightly lit room from a dark corridor. At first people blink and look away, perhaps defending themselves from the harsh new light by placing their hand over their face. It is only over time that they are able to fully open their eyes. The first level of the assimilation process is, as I have described, one in which people are able to catch a glimpse of their dementia, but then instinctively turn away from it – and may perhaps instead talk about it only indirectly. While they have an awareness of the problem, the person struggles to put this into words properly and instead dementia is reduced to an 'it' – a thing that is painful to name. The emotional distress engendered by their dementia, and their struggles to reduce the intensity of these feelings, means that the person seems to be on edge – they can fear they are on the brink of losing control and being overwhelmed by the dementia.

Some people that I have worked with were not able to move past this position: their dementia was too frightening to face and instead their life (and often that of their family and friends) was devoted to avoiding reminders, and thus reducing the possibility that they would be distressed by it. However, other clients have been able to move beyond this and to begin, gradually, to put a name to their dementia while also retaining some control over their feelings. Stiles refers to this level as one that involves the development of a vague awareness that there is something wrong. As the case example of Sonia illustrates well, people tend to move backwards and forwards between the different levels of the assimilation model – a therapeutic trend that is amplified by the difficulties that people with dementia have in holding onto their memories.

In this level, the existence of the *problematic voice* (which says that something is wrong) is acknowledged but this remains uncomfortable, and it cannot yet be fully articulated. However, the individual is capable of discussing the problem even if it can be distressing to do this. People who are working at this level, therefore, manage to acknowledge the existence of problems related to dementia and will acknowledge that Alzheimer's disease or dementia exists but tend to talk about this in general terms and will, for the most part, still not be able to apply these terms to their own problems. Instead, they may describe behaviours or episodes from their daily life that were unexpected and which they cannot fully explain. Thus, one man in a group that I worked with spoke about having a visual hallucination, which was probably part of his Lewy body dementia:

> 'I seem to see people who aren't there, and I don't know why. The other day I was walking along, and thought there was someone beside me – I was sure of it, and said "hello" – but when they didn't answer I turned around, and there was nobody there.'

In therapy, clients may be caught up in the moment of the pain, loss and anger that arises from their dementia and will often bring this distress into the therapeutic space with tears of sadness or frustration being common at this point. Often people will talk about feeling stupid, silly, hurt, sad, angry and struggle to step away from this distress. As Mr D told his therapy group during the Dementia Voice project:

> But it's the, it's the quality of the emotions inside me that really, really gets to me. Because I think I've done something terribly wrong. Not wrong entirely wrong, it's just that it goes wrong. I mean today, I didn't have a clue where I was going to go to put my car. I don't think that comes into your, your er, and as soon as that started, I just felt ridiculous. I can't describe how really, really stupid I felt.

Although the client may acknowledge or refer to the existence of problems related to dementia (the *problematic voice*), the possibility of dementia as being relevant or as an explanation for the person's problems is not considered or is rejected (the *dominant voice*). Thus, when the other participants in Mr B's therapy group started to talk about having dementia, Mr B was clearly irritated and remonstrated with them:

> But there's a premise here, that I just don't agree with the way you're talking it sounds like you've accepted the fact that you've got Alzheimer's. Now I don't think anyone in this room has got Alzheimer's.

While Mr B, at this stage of the group, did not connect his problems with dementia, he was able to identify symptoms that concerned him:

> On the subject of Christmas cards. I mean it illustrates in a way that this problem is short-term memory. My wife will give me a list and I will write most of the envelopes and any personal message inside and then I think it's ready for posting and I'll completely forget to put any stamps on them yet. You know it's silly really and my wife will say, 'You haven't got any stamps.' It's just as likely that I will take the whole lot down and post them without any stamps on them.

This strong sense of ambivalence about dementia has been documented in qualitative analyses of the accounts of people living with dementia. For Linda

Clare (Clare, 2002, 2003; Clare and Wilson, 2006), for instance, the central dynamic in participants' descriptions of their dementia was a tension between their attempts to protect the self from the threat of dementia and the need for them to integrate aspects of their experiences into their self concept. In one study (Robinson et al., 2005), nine older couples were interviewed. The authors outlined a circular model of coping based around a dual-process model of grieving with couples moving from denial, avoidance and minimization of problems into a gradual acceptance of these changes. Just as Stiles described his psychotherapy clients as alternating between the *problematic* and *dominant voices* within this level of assimilation, so Robinson et al. described an oscillating process of first pushing away and then accepting parts of the experience. For them this was characterized by:

> .... *a cyclical process of denial, minimization and gradual realization as couples gradually began to accept the changes in the person with dementia were likely to be permanent, linked to an oscillating process of acknowledging what had been lost, as well as carrying on as a couple.* (Robinson et al., 2005, p. 344)

Working with ambivalence

In working with people who have a vague awareness of their dementia, the chief task of a therapist is to help their client to place some form on their expressions of problematic material, while containing the distress and anxiety associated with this. Consequently, it is important to ensure that the therapeutic work is predictable and that this occurs within secure boundaries, and in the context of a strong therapeutic relationship. Where possible, therapists should also consider mobilizing and addressing any external resources that might support the person at this time – and similarly address any dynamics within relationships that might act as barriers to further assimilation.

Given that the hallmark of this level of assimilation is the presence of powerful emotions, a key feature of my work with people who were operating at this level was to find a way to notice their distress and to help them to move through this. In many ways, this is a similar reflective technique to the noticing of the symptoms of dementia that I outlined as being appropriate with people operating primarily at lower levels of assimilation. However, the focus here is on the person's affective rather than their behavioural response, and in doing this it is also possible to tentatively offer a potential cause for distress. Thus, a typical response might be: '*I can see that you're upset about your poor memory. I know that some people worry that a poor memory is a sign of dementia and I wondered if this had ever crossed your mind?*' Suggestions such as this can enable clients to step back from their emotions and to begin to talk about their reaction to dementia. They both identify a putative explanation for the person's distress and also facilitate the person in distancing themselves from their distress.

It is also important to recognize that the person will be ambivalent about their dementia, both wanting to know but also scared of finding out. It is only possible for a client to approach their dementia, and to begin to reflect on its impact, if they also know that they can stop talking about this and turn their attention away. We therefore need to find ways to allow this emotional escape or retreat from their dementia. Therapeutically, we should err towards walking alongside the person in their discovery of dementia, rather than simply leading them towards it. However, there may be occasions where it is necessary to provide factual information about the person's diagnosis. A client may have forgotten, for instance, a different aspect of their assessment, or not know their diagnosis or when they had received this. It is important, therefore, to either know this information or to have ready access to it. On occasions I have been able to talk over the results of a cognitive assessment or scan with a client in the memory clinic, sharing this information with them as appropriate at their request and within the context of a discussion about their fears. In a similar vein, clients may also comment on their prognosis or ask for clarification about this and here it is important for therapists to be clear that all forms of dementia are progressive and untreatable. These are uncomfortable messages to give, but providing straightforward factual answers is a vital element of building a trusting therapeutic relationship.

Final words

There are many good reasons why people living with dementia do so without talking about or noticing the existence of either the symptoms of dementia or the label of an illness such as Alzheimer's disease. Neuropsychological impairment, including the continual eroding of a person's ability to recall recent memories and to find words to describe their experiences, clearly play important roles and I will consider how therapists may try to work around these limitations in Chapter 11. There are also personal and social factors that may mean that a person is unable to accommodate such a profound change in their life. These issues will be considered in more detail in Chapter 12. However, many other people find ways to make sense of what is happening to them by addressing a dilemma: whether to confront the threat posed by the diagnosis or instead push this knowledge out of their mind. Each course of action comes with risks: while it might sometimes be preferable not to think about the dementia, this reduces the person's ability to adjust to the condition. At the same time, engaging with dementia is painful and distressing.

In this chapter I have outlined how a therapist can work with people who are struggling with this dilemma. While many people are able to name their dementia without external aid, for others sensitive, compassionate and thoughtful therapeutic support can help them with this task. In the next chapter I will turn to supporting people who are operating at this level of assimilation.

9 Finding distance and perspective

'You asked me once, what was in Room 101. I told you that you knew the answer already. Everyone knows it. The thing that is in Room 101 is the worst thing in the world.'

(O'Brien, from 1984 by George Orwell)

The climax of Orwell's novel *1984* sees the book's protagonist, Winston Smith, facing interrogation in the basement torture chamber of the Ministry of Love – the prosaically named Room 101. The contents of Room 101 vary for each prisoner who is brought there – because for each of them the Party brings a prisoner face-to-face with their own worst nightmare, fear or phobia in order to break them down and overcome their resistance. Thus, Winston Smith is tortured and emotionally overwhelmed by his greatest fear – that of rats.

I have come to believe that the prospect of dementia acts in the same way to Room 101 – we each of us bring our own worst fears to dementia. The task for people living with dementia is, like Winston Smith, to confront their fears about it and to find a way, at least for some of the time, to live alongside those fears. For each person, the worst aspect of dementia will vary – for some it may be a fear of losing their sense of who they are, for others it might be a loss of dignity, or a fear of becoming mad. The problematic aspects of dementia that each person confronts will differ and the therapeutic task is to help the person to talk about this because the act of talking about it – naming this dementia – may help them to step back from it and thus to begin to find some control over it.

This phase of assimilation comprises two levels. In the first, the person is able to name their dementia, and uses terms such as Alzheimer's disease to apply to themselves. In the second level, the client is not only able to talk about their dementia, but also begins to find some emotional distance from their diagnosis. This ability to distance oneself from the problematic experience of dementia may be achieved in different ways: for some it is by identifying those aspects of dementia that they find most difficult, while for others distance is achieved by making links with other areas of their life. Table 9.1 summarizes these two different levels and the tasks associated with each.

Table 9.1 Therapeutic tasks and strategies at the different assimilation levels during the distancing phase

Assimilation level	Behaviour and affect	Therapeutic task of client	Therapeutic task of therapist	Possible interventions
3. Problem clarification	Client begins to talk about dementia. Affect is negative but manageable.	To give a name to their dementia-related experiences, and to identify themselves as having dementia.	To explore the problematic aspects of dementia-related experiences and work to establish distance from these feelings.	Encourage exploration of dementia-related experiences, e.g., provide information, attendance at an Alzheimer's café. Introduce tasks for the client and their family, for instance to identify goals. Identify the problematic elements (e.g., fear of dependency).
4. Understanding or insight	Person looks for help and support. Affect is mixed – increasingly business-like.	To step back from dementia-related experiences and to make links with other aspects of life – including identifying the problematic aspects of dementia.	To support the client in addressing problematic experiences.	Consolidate attempts to address dementia. Encourage discussion about appropriate care in the present, and the future. Discuss disclosing the diagnosis to family and friends.

Level 3: Problem clarification

As I outlined in Chapter 8, people who are working at the vague awareness level of assimilation can acknowledge that there is something wrong in their lives but are not yet in a position where they can name this problem as dementia. However, this position of knowing but not naming is difficult to maintain, as an awareness of a problem invites speculation about its causes. Consequently, as the person's ability to acknowledge their dementia grows in strength (the *problematic voice*), so the response of the *dominant voice* becomes more distinct, often leading to direct conflict between the voices. We can see this conflict between these distinct positions when people report having mixed feelings about their dementia, or describe often intense feelings of being silly, angry or stuck. Unlike Level 2 (vague awareness), there is a clear statement of the problem, and the person is able to talk about the impact that dementia is having on them, even if these feelings are often powerfully expressed.

One example of the intense confusion of the conflicting *problematic* and *dominant voices* comes from Val, a client who described the panic that engulfed her when she went shopping:

> I went into the local shop, around the corner from ours and I got to the front of the queue, and they asked me for my money, and I couldn't find it. I didn't know what I wanted or where I was, so I ran out, and my husband was there. He said, "What are you making such a fuss about?" He always treats me as if I'm a little girl, it's embarrassing, but he's right – I need to try harder and to do things, but I'm scared to do them, so I don't know what to do.

Here Val seems to be describing both that she is frightened by her difficulties in paying for her shopping (a *problematic voice*), and that she needs to try harder (a *dominant voice*), which was triggered by her husband's dismissive comment. Val articulates a sense of being stuck between these two conflicting voices.

Self-evaluative split

Sometimes, in articulating their mixed feelings about aspects of their dementia, clients will use discursive connectors that indicate these conflicting ways to approach their dementia. Often this will take the form of a 'yes ... but' statement, as for instance when Edward told me, '*I suppose I'm feeling a bit silly when I've forgotten ... Well I realize I'm being silly, but even so I get a bit cross at times.*' When I asked him who he was cross with he replied, '*I suppose it is against myself and I'm also, initially, I'm cross with the person who reminds me [laughs].*'

Clients working at this level are approaching an identification of what it is about dementia that is difficult for them to tolerate. For some people with dementia it is the lack of a cure that makes dementia intolerable, while for others it may be the prospect of deterioration or feeling guilty and embarrassed at the impact of their dementia on their family. Thus, clients working at this level are able to make a statement of the way in which dementia represents a problem for them, even if this is mentioned indirectly rather than being completely articulated. There is no sense at this level of how to find a way through this problem. As Mrs H in the Dementia Voice project explained:

> I'm just going to sit back and let nature take its course, I think, and then if it gets really bad, I'll wear a notice, but I haven't yet worked out what I'm going to put on that notice [laughs], but it depends on my mood I should think. But no, I must admit to keeping it as quiet as possible. I push it to the back I must admit. I don't sort of analyse it. I think probably you know, I'm whatever it is, 94 or something you know [laughs]. I just let it go over me. Yes, really, I do. I don't pay too much attention to it at all. My life goes on very much in the same way as it always has been. So, whether that means that I'm just unfeeling in

all situations, but I don't feel it would, or whether it just means that, I don't know if it's a weak nature, and I can't do anything about this [laughs] but I mean it does bring some peace of mind sometimes.

Describing feelings about feelings around dementia

Another indicator that a client is working at this level comes when they describe both an emotional response to their dementia, and also their response to this. As Donald, a man with significant communication problems told me about his experiences of coming to a therapy group:

Well to me, I just, it was frightening really, because I just didn't know what was happening and I thought, 'Well, has something happened which I can't get back. Am I going to sort of have to go in a home and sit down there until I die sort of thing?' A lot of things go through your head, and you just have to work it out. When I came to you, I mean I could see that there was other people there with exactly the same thing ... I could feel that by talking to those, they were in virtually the same position as I was. You know I mean they were having trouble and I was having trouble. So, I'm not being sort of out-talked all the time by these because I can keep my thing in there and as I've found out now because of you I can now go in and sort of take the realm (sic) and talk to them. Well, you already know this, but the biggest thing was to me was that I was going to go down and be a loony, and they were all going to go 'yer, yer, yer' [gestures with index finger of hand, pointing and rotating it against his head].

Building emotional distance from dementia

Once clients have recognized and named their dementia, so it is important to help them to gain distance and perspective from their feelings about this. We can see this process of distancing occurring when a client moves from expressing or enacting their feelings about dementia (for instance by crying), to stepping back and talking about what it is about the dementia that makes them cry. This is a subtle but important distinction. There are many different ways in which people distance themselves from their dementia. Some people joke about their mistakes, others reflect on their life and remind themselves that in some ways they are fortunate, while others take comfort in finding out that they are not alone. In my experience, these tasks were often more easily accomplished within the context of a group. This gives participants an opportunity to listen to their peers talk about their fears of deterioration or experiences of shame and embarrassment. I will consider this process in more detail later in this chapter when I discuss how Mr B was able to move away from warding off his dementia.

It can also help the person to make links or gain perspective by asking them to think more fully about their feelings, for instance by asking questions such as: *'Is it always like that?'* or *'Are there times when life is better for you?'* In this way, the therapist is working with the client to help them to explore their dementia, differentiating between occasions when it is easier to tolerate, searching for other perspectives on their condition and looking for strategies that mitigate their distress. It may also be useful at this stage to encourage clients to explore their dementia further, for instance by attending community services including Alzheimer cafés or Singing for the Brain groups.

Level 4: Understanding or insight

The therapeutic task within the problem clarification stage of the assimilation model (Level 3) is for people to continue to name their dementia while beginning to find some emotional distance from it. The next stage of understanding and insight (Level 4) is characterized therefore, by just such an emotional distance. This can be seen in therapy when clients identify the dementia-associated experiences that they find most difficult (understanding) or when they reflect on how the feelings that dementia creates touch upon aspects of living that they have always found difficult (insight). This aspect of therapy has sometimes been referred to as an *'aha'* moment – when the person connects the dots in their life (Mosak, 2014).

Understanding

The feature that distinguishes this level is that the individual with dementia understands how their feelings about dementia relate to their wider life – for instance how it creates some feelings (e.g., being embarrassed), which they then try to manage. Alternatively, the person may describe how interpersonal relationships are affected, both by their own way of coping with dementia and by the changes in how others relate to them. In this way, the individual accepts other people's reactions, rather than rebelling against them, and has some understanding of how to move forward. This understanding enables the person to move away from being emotionally overwhelmed by the dementia and instead to step back from these feelings. In contrast to previous levels, which are characterized by a sense of being stuck, clients are able to express a sense that their feelings around the dementia can be managed. As Edith told her group:

> I know that my husband finds it hard when I can't remember things, it must be awful for him. So, I try not to say anything at those times, or to go to my room when I want to cry. I know that it's silly, to have to cry, but I want to hide it from him, so that he doesn't worry. He's got enough to put up with, and even if it makes me feel a bit more lonely, well I feel that at least I'm doing something for him for a change.

Insight

From the perspective of the assimilation model, the development of insight is not just about a person recognizing that they have dementia, but also involves an articulated understanding of what the problematic aspects of that illness are. This might include understanding how their response to dementia may be shaped by concerns they have had throughout their life. Thus, in the Dementia Voice project, Mr B told his group:

> You see I think the essential difference is that I was brought up as a boy to learn to stand on your own two feet. In the navy the whole basis of the navy training is that every man jack on board should stand up on his own two feet. So fundamentally, you develop this idea that other people are around and are very useful and helpful, particularly if they are doing things that you want them to do. But the idea that you can actually begin to rely on other people to do things that you don't want to, or you can't remember how, or you didn't have any intention to do anyway, is something I've begun to learn in the last four or five years. I've been a very independent soul all my life – even independent to a large extent from my wife. I mean we're very close – we always have been close – but we're closer. I hate the word intellectually, but we're closer now than ever before because of this.

The person's affective level may be mixed with some unpleasant recognition, but with curiosity and even pleasant surprise as they begin to make sense out of the emotions that the dementia has provoked. Often the process of gaining distance can be augmented through the use of humour or by comparing themselves with others in a worse position. Thus, Mr D described how he used humour as a way of stepping back:

> I've taken the view, when I first arrived there, I had very little idea about what was going on. It was probably not until she [Mrs H] popped along, we had spoken about various things I became more, what's the word, I was more aware, I think. When I first walked in there, but after a very, very short period of time, we had a good laugh. And it was to me just what I wanted to see and hear ... I think the difference is being, it's a continuation of Alzheimer's if you like. You could say, you could just say that it makes me feel good. Even though I know I've got Alzheimer's, I can still laugh, I don't have to just sit here and go, 'Oh God.

At this level the person is able to acknowledge both the dementia and their dominant (e.g., fearful, ashamed or angry) reaction to this, but to distance themselves from this reaction, either by setting out how different situations produce different responses, or by describing ways in which they can switch from one internal state to another. Within therapy the client with dementia may be able to describe how being with others who experience the same problems is different to being at home or with strangers. Thus, participants in two different groups that I led both contrasted the openness of the group and their life away from this therapeutic environment:

> Edith: *Knowing that you're all the same [in the group] so you don't feel too embarrassed. My family and that, they don't know how to handle it. I can't go out on my own. I always have to go out with someone in case I have that feeling [having a panic attack]. I'm scared.*

And

> Doreen: *It's important to be able to come and open my mind. If I was to say these things back where I live, to talk to other people there as I talk here, then I would be embarrassed. I would worry that they would all think that I was doolally.*

Facilitating understanding and insight

The central therapeutic task when working with people at this level of assimilation is to help them to continue to process the problematic experiences. Often simple counselling techniques, such as reflection, can facilitate this. For instance, Mr B's insight above that his dementia meant that he needed to overcome his lifelong tendency towards independence was prompted by my reflecting back on a previous statement of his and being curious as to its significance: '*I was interested to hear you say that learning to rely on other people had been quite surprisingly – I'm not sure I can remember exactly the words you used – pleasant? Easy? Learning that other people would do things for you. Has it always been easy?*' The need for therapists to act as a therapeutic memory bank – recalling previously articulated voices and reflecting on these at opportune moments – is intensified when working with people living with dementia.

Therapists can also help to consolidate the person's distancing from their emotional responses to their dementia by bringing the focus in therapy onto practical ways of coping with dementia. This could include discussing decisions around driving, preparing wills or a legal power of attorney, and who they have told about the dementia. All of these issues can prompt powerful emotional reactions, as they involve engaging with, respectively, loss of independence and identity, prognosis and shame. Sometimes, where groups are established and in a position to be able to work together effectively, by touching on one issue we can prompt further work – in much the same way that a snowball can touch off an avalanche. Thus, Mr B, in the fourth session of a group in the Dementia Voice project (Watkins et al., 2006) challenged the group by stating: '*Now there's a premise here that I just don't agree with. The way you're talking, you sound as though you've accepted the fact that you've got Alzheimer's. Now I don't think anyone in this room has got Alzheimer's.*' This acted as a catalyst enabling other members of the group both to describe themselves as having Alzheimer's disease and to explore how feelings of shame made them reluctant to tell others. This in turn prompted Mrs H to reflect on her own emotional reaction to dementia:

Mrs H: *And I just wonder where it's going to end, that's my fear*

Mr B: *When it's going to end?*

Mrs H: *Where it is going to end, you know. Where am I going to end up, just before the end, you know?*

Mrs A: *Oh, I see you mean. I talk about death, to my family and I think that the only thing that I'm frightened of is the unknown and that is death to me.*

Mr H: *Oh no, I'm worried about what comes just before [laughs]. It could be years before, couldn't it? Oh years.*

Mr B: *Is it the dying that?*

Mrs H: *No, no, I don't feel that at all, no, because we all go through that. No I'm not frightened about that. No. I mean it's not really my religion to say it at all, but I don't know if there's anything else and I'm not going to worry about that right now, you know.*

Facilitator: *So, what is the frightening, when you say about the future?*

Mrs H: *Being, being useless, you know. Not having all my faculties. I dread that, I dread that. It's as if I'm going to sort of come to it one morning, perhaps, you know and think, 'Oh my godfathers, what's left? You know I really worry about that.*

As a facilitator, it is important to focus on staying with clients as they explore their own distress. In the example above, Mr B, whose initial assertion that nobody in the group had Alzheimer's disease had prompted these exchanges, returned the following week and began the session in a contained, but nevertheless angry manner by taking a piece of paper from his pocket on which he had made notes and reading these out. He complained that in the previous week he felt the group had made a crucial mistake, that it had become confused and equated having a poor memory with a lack of intelligence. Mr B went onto say: *'Now the problem with Alzheimer's as it is affects me is that I have no problems with retrieving the information in the long term ... even the most intelligent set of people, who can still do a crossword puzzle, etc. can still have Alzheimer's. It's got nothing to do with intelligence – it's short-term memory only.'*

This change in Mr B's tone marked an important shift in the way in which he described his dementia, which in our analysis was rated as being at Level 3 (problem clarification). However, Mr B's description of his dementia continued to evolve: in the seventh week he once again referred directly to his dementia, but rather than the angry, almost confrontational tone of the fifth week, Mr B now made a joke of his dementia: *'Can I tell you something that's happened to me in this last week? I've had a CT scan ... I got the results back yesterday and it said that my brain had shrunk very, very slightly in the cavity, which is fairly symptomatic of the onset of Alzheimer's ... It's still twice as big as everyone else's so it's quite alright.'*

This seemed to be a clear indication of Mr B using humour as a way of gaining distance and perspective on his dementia. He had been able to move from seeing Alzheimer's disease as something that happened to other people to a position where he was able to make a joke about his brain having shrunk and that this was *'symptomatic'* of the illness. He was able to name Alzheimer's disease, but without being emotionally overwhelmed by this. As is often the case in psychotherapy, it's difficult to be certain about what had helped Mr B to talk in such a different way. However, there are some clues about how dementia came to have a new meaning for him: as Mr B himself reflected in the penultimate session, dementia no longer seemed as threatening to him: *'I don't see the problem now. It frightened me, the problem of declining memory, until I came here, and now I'm not frightened. It frightened me because I thought, well, "I'm going mad, I'm going crazy". What am I going to be like in another five years? But now I realize that everybody is getting this problem.'*

So what was it that helped Mr B to realize that he was not going mad? He himself related this to the support the group had provided saying, *'I've got a great deal of moral uplift by coming here, meeting you, listening to the way you do it.'* The most likely explanation seems to be that it had something to do with listening to the other group participants describing their sense of shame or embarrassment and to Mrs H describing her fears for the future. This conversation seems to have spoken to Mr B in an important way, as it is in the session immediately after these interactions that he acknowledged for the first time that he had Alzheimer's disease, and angrily asserted that a poor short-term memory should not be equated with being stupid. Importantly in Mr B's reflection in Week 9, his description of overcoming his worries about what he might be like in five years' time almost exactly mirrors Mrs H's comments in Week 4 about her fears for what she might become. As Mr B remarked, *'Once I've made my mind up about that* [being forgetful doesn't mean you're stupid], *I don't get depressed by it.'*

Asking about previous experiences of dementia

For many of us, our first experience of dementia comes from knowing a relative or neighbour who has developed Alzheimer's disease or a related illness. More than half the population of the UK know someone who has dementia (Alzheimer's Research UK, 2022b). People who have personal experience of dementia in this way are more likely to worry about developing dementia themselves (Lee et al., 2020) and to be less comfortable around people with dementia (Ebert et al., 2020). It is often important, therefore, for therapists to be curious with clients as to how these experiences impact on their feelings about their own dementia now. One man I worked with, for instance, told me that his greatest fears were that he would in the future become violent and assault his wife, as his *'much-loved'* uncle had assaulted his aunt. In a similar way Sue, interviewed with her husband by Katie Snow (Snow et al., 2015), revealed that her fears about the future were shaped in part by her experiences of her father-in-law:

> I mean, physically could I mean, ah. I think that's the biggest worry I think anybody with mental health has – that physically your body could go on longer than your brain and then you cease to be … you, you're just a function, like your Daddy was in the end, just a function and that's what I don't want. I think my problem is we nursed Peter's father through Alzheimer's didn't we? so you know how that particular disease progresses and you, you don't really want to be reminded that's maybe the way I go.

Identifying these fears in therapy enables us to continue to have conversations about the rational basis for them – what would constitute, for instance, losing (and retaining) function – and if appropriate, sharing these concerns with other members of the family.

Reflecting on stigma and shame

As we have seen in the series of exchanges that led Mr B to move from pushing his fears about dementia away to acknowledging and making sense of them, encouraging clients to talk about whether they feel ashamed can be an important therapeutic step (Aldridge et al., 2019; Cheston, 2005). Importantly, experiences of shame can act to block the therapeutic processes (Gilbert, 1997). At the same time, these can by their nature be sensitive topics to enquire about, in part because to do so can be interpreted by clients as if their therapist is suggesting that there was an aspect of their lives that they should feel ashamed about.

One way to bring this into the conversation and which, with Ann Marshall, I have incorporated into the LivDem course (see Chapter 6) is to reflect on the number of well-known people who have been diagnosed with Alzheimer's disease or another form of dementia. This includes footballers (e.g., members of the England 1966 World Cup team including Jackie and Bobby Charlton), actors (e.g., Prunella Scales and Barbara Windsor) and politicians such as Margaret Thatcher and Ronald Reagan. Bringing these figures into the conversation both humanizes dementia and enables a discussion about social attitudes – for instance whether public perceptions of these people are indeed affected by knowledge of their illness.

In a similar way, introducing people whose dementia is likely to have been triggered by their profession such as footballers, rugby players and American footballers, facilitates a conversation about the causes of dementia. Many people that I have worked with have been frightened that their dementia was genetically inherited and were concerned, therefore, that they might have

unwittingly passed this on to their children and grandchildren. Actively addressing this and providing factual information about the risk factors around their
form of dementia meant that I could actively challenge some of these misrepre-
sentations.

In these discussions about social attitudes, it is important to be sensitive to
potential indications that participants may be experiencing shame. By its
nature, this will often be hidden so that therapists need to be mindful of potential cues that clients are experiencing shame (Retzinger, 1991, 1995). These
include references to being 'silly' or anger and avoidance of issues. There are
also visual cues such as hiding or masking behaviour, such as the hand covering all or parts of the face, or when clients avert their gaze, lower their eyes or
blush. These cues are context-related and often appear in a cluster. The more
potential cues of shame that you encounter, then the stronger the evidence that
this may be experienced by clients.

Final words

I began this chapter by discussing how the *1984* character, Winston Smith, was
tortured in the Ministry of Love by being threatened with Room 101. In the
novel, Winston is broken by this – he gives up his struggle against Big Brother
whom he now embraces. In suggesting that dementia represents something of
a similar challenge, we need to recognize that many people make a choice not
to look into their dementia. Importantly, it is possible to enjoy a good quality of
life without talking openly about the existence of dementia. These are choices
that as therapists we must acknowledge and accept. We need, therefore, to feel
our way carefully and slowly into a conversation and to give our clients the
opportunity to withdraw and turn away from their dementia. As I will explore
in more depth in Chapter 12, this is not a conversational road that everyone will
either want or need to travel down.

At the same time, however, many people living with dementia do want to
make sense out of what is happening to them. Our task as therapists is to help
them to do just this by enabling them to step back and to find distance from
their distress. In the next chapter I will look at how we can continue to support
people to live well with their dementia and to integrate this into their wider
identity.

10   'Working through' and finding partial solutions

The reality of death destroys me, but the idea of death saves me ... The way to value life, the way to feel compassion for others, the way to love anything with greatest depth is to be aware that these experiences are destined to be lost.

Irvin Yalom (2008)

The American psychotherapist Irvin Yalom describes how, for some people, confrontation with an urgent, life-changing event can act not just as a trauma but as the catalyst to jerk a person out of their everyday existence, and their habitual pattern of leading their life, and can precipitate a profound change in the way in which they live their life. He terms these as *'awakening experiences'* and suggests that they can be precipitated by a diagnosis of a life-threatening illness, bereavement or a milestone birthday (e.g., passing the age of 50).

> *While working intensively over a 10-year period with patients facing death from cancer, I found that many of them, rather than succumb to numbing despair, were positively and dramatically transformed. They rearranged their life priorities by trivialising life's trivia. They assumed the power not to do the things they really didn't want to do. They communicated more deeply with those they loved and appreciated more keenly the elemental facts of life – the changing seasons, the beauty of nature, the last Christmas or New Year.* (page 34)

In a similar way to Yalom, I too have encountered people living with dementia who have also experienced such a transformation in their lives and who made decisions to invest themselves in savouring life and their closest relationships while they were still able to do so. For all of these clients, these decisions were made within the context of talking about their dementia in a series of psychotherapy sessions – often with their partner – and working through the implications of their dementia. However, there are also many other examples of people living with dementia talking about themselves in a way that I think Yalom would recognize. The Scottish dementia advocate, James McKillop for instance, has written (McKillop, 2003):

> *Being told I had dementia was like a door re-opening after a difficult time in my life – new challenges, new opportunities ... I want people to understand that dementia isn't an end, it's a new beginning where you do things differently.*

In the assimilation model, Stiles sets out three levels in which people work to understand the root of their problems and work through these: Level 5, which refers to finding partial solutions; Level 6, which concerns problem solution; and Level 7, which relates to mastery. However, I have chosen to bring these into a single phase that involves working through and finding partial solutions. This is because, in practice, I found it hard to distinguish between responses at these different levels – possibly because the challenges that people with dementia face differ in an important way from that which most psychotherapy clients have to deal with, in that dementia is both progressive and threatens the most fundamental elements of the person's being, including their capacity to make sense of what they face.

In the higher levels of the assimilation model, the person with dementia is able to find partial solutions to their problems, for instance through making decisions about their life and their care. Often, they are able to talk about having made a change in how they understand their life and their dementia and how others see them. At the same time, people understand that the problem of dementia has not left them and that, indeed, their physical and mental well-being will deteriorate. Clients who work at this level are able to integrate the *problematic* and the *dominant voices* in order to make tangible progress towards resolving those problems that occur in daily living. This new understanding is used to work on a problem in which the client may describe considering alternatives. Their affect is positive, business-like, and optimistic even though these decisions are being taken in the awareness that the larger problem of dementia cannot be avoided. These clients recognize both that this can be only a partial or unsuccessful solution, yet also manage to express hope for the future (Wolverson et al., 2010). As one man said in his feedback on a LivDem group he attended (see Chapter 6): '*the group has been a helpful place*

Table 10.1 Therapeutic tasks and strategies during the 'working through' phase

Assimilation level	Behaviour and affect	Therapeutic task of client	Therapeutic task of therapist	Possible interventions
5. 'Working through' and finding partial solutions	Client acknowledges the existence of a dementia, and that the dementia cannot be cured but can be managed. Allows others to care for them, gives up control when appropriate and weighs up attempts at a specific or partial solution to different problems. May be hopeful about their future.	To prepare for the future and manage the present in the light of the diagnosis.	To help the client to address any choices they need to make about their life.	Plan tasks to accommodate cognitive impairments. Make practical preparations for the future, e.g., make a living will, assign legal power of attorney, giving up driving. Identify healthy living strategies and ways to stay active. Discuss activities that make life meaningful.

to share information and get tips! It's helped me develop confidence to move forward and keep doing things in spite of my dementia.'

That people living with dementia may be hopeful is, at first sight, a counter-intuitive proposition. How is it possible to have a genuine sense of optimism, while at the same time recognizing that the illness that you have is progressive, destructive and incurable? At one level, optimism necessitates a need to live in a narrower temporal framework, and to focus on more immediate goals (Cheston, 2010). As Ron commented in one group: *'Some people there when they're told they've got Alzheimer's feel like they're going to die tomorrow. And you're not going to die tomorrow of Alzheimer's, you will die at some point, but not tomorrow, and you've still got a life to live, and you can manage to do so many things.'* Similarly, this exchange between two participants in the Dementia Voice project illustrates how hope can be focused on finding an acceptable way to live within the shadow of dementia:

Mrs A: *Is it hope that's got something to do with your present outlook?*

Mr B: *Hope for what?*

Mrs A: *Hope for anything that's in Pandora's box.*

Mr B: *Yes, but you, hope has got to be attached to something. When you say hope left, you've got to say ... hope for what? Now, have I got hope that this problem will go away? No. Have I got hope that there will be a, that we will evolve a way of living with it? Yes, I have, high hope that we can do that.*

As Mr B shows in this extract, people with dementia who are working at this level acknowledge the existence of a dementia which they explicitly recognize cannot be cured but instead focus on managing this. They allow others to care for them where necessary, giving up control when appropriate and weighing up attempts at a specific or partial solution to different problems. Clients who talk about themselves at this level often describe feeling positive (including a sense of pride or accomplishment) about having changed in their relationship with their dementia. This may include trying out a new strategy or describing a more subtle change, such as a change in how they understand and feel about their illness. This accomplishment and change is important to the client, and their affect reflects this as it tends towards being positive, satisfied and proud of achievements. As part of this process, the client may reflect on a specific change in which an aspect of their dementia that had previously been problematic has now been integrated. In one of our final sessions, one participant reflected on how he had changed:

Yes. Well, it's an illness. It's something of the body not working properly and if your appendix isn't working properly, you go and have it seen to, don't you? Anything that isn't working properly, you get it put right. And you may not do it easily, and some things you can't get put right, but I think we've come a long way to cope with the problems we've got. And I'm personally very grateful.

I feel much better about things than I did when I first started ... You have to develop techniques to help you to remember. Even if it means writing notes down on a pad or ... recording it on a machine or pinning it on a board, or something. We all have to do those things and that is what I think is the only solution. You can't bring this memory back; the brain is gone in that respect.

These changes may be noticed by other people. Here is an example of how Mr B, from the Dementia Voice project, noticed change in one of the other participants:

Mrs A: *I've met a lot of people who are rather ashamed of not being like everybody else, but I mean none of us are like everybody else —*

Mrs F: *I was like that ... I was just saying I didn't want anybody to know anything about it ... Not going out the front door – being ashamed of the name and ...*

Mr B: *I think F has changed probably more than anyone else, do you? I think that F has got to grips with the problem very well indeed, you've gone much more extraverted than when you first started. You talk to everyone now. You say what you think.*

For Stiles and his colleagues, the final level of mastery represented the point at which the psychotherapy patient no longer needed to continue to work on a problem – it had ceased to be of concern to them, and its emotional force had been spent. As such, it is a level that does not translate easily into dementia care, because by its progressive nature and profound emotional threat, dementia will continue to represent a continually evolving threat to well-being. However, although rare, there do seem to be some examples that suggest that the person who is working at this level is able to integrate dementia into the whole of their life. The existence of dementia is acknowledged and recognized but no longer defines them as a person. We might expect that the emotional aspects of that change for themselves and for others are also recognized, and that the person's affect is positive. At the end of a psychotherapy group, Dave spoke about how he had changed his life after addressing his fears about dementia:

Dave: *What will be, will be. There's nothing you can do about this except to try and make the most of each day as it comes, and to let your mind go free. I know that what's going to come will be difficult, but I will accept it at the time. It's still the same old me in here, and once you put your mind to it, life carries on.*

Supporting people to live in the shadow of dementia

The central therapeutic task in working with people who have dementia and who are able to acknowledge their dementia is to support them in making decisions about their life. In my experience there are five important areas to focus on:

1 *Addressing psychological needs.* For many people, the process of acknowledging their dementia also invites the ghosts of buried psychological pain into their lives. This may take the form of a shameful response at the perceived exposure of a flaw, panic at the thought of future disintegration or a sense of abandonment. When this occurs, it is important to draw upon those generic psychotherapy skills that are most appropriate, and shift from a focus on dementia, to a wider search for meaning, compassion and forgiveness. In this context, psychotherapy with people living with dementia often draws on similar skill sets to those needed within any form of palliative care.

2 *Enhancing psychological resilience.* The theme of resilience is one of the most widely explored research topics in gerontology. Higher levels of resilience have been associated with a range of positive outcomes including successful ageing, better emotional adjustment and longer life (MacLeod et al., 2016). However, resilience is a difficult concept to define, and partly because of this, it can be difficult to develop interventions that can enhance it. However, research from social psychology (Wildschut et al., 2006; Routledge et al., 2013) suggests that it may be helpful to define resilience in terms of five different elements of psychological resource: enhancing self-esteem, building meaning in life, maintaining social connectedness, increasing optimism and strengthening self-continuity. As I described in Chapter 3, together with my colleagues at the University of the West of England and the University of Southampton I have begun to translate this research into dementia care (Cheston et al., 2015). We began by replicating research showing that when we strengthened these psychological resources (through the medium of asking people with dementia to recall a nostalgia memory) then people with dementia were able to recall more information about their dementia without at the same time becoming more distressed (Ismail et al., 2018). While our current research programme involves seeing if it is feasible to help people with dementia to draw on nostalgic memories in their day-to-day lives (Dodd et al., 2022; Ismail et al., 2018), there are many other ways to enhance these key resources. A study of 53 people who had recently been diagnosed with dementia (Cotter et al., 2018), for instance, showed that individuals with higher levels of hope had a greater sense of self-worth or positive feelings about themselves. The authors suggest that higher levels of hope may help the individual balance the potential threats to self-esteem and aid adjustment. Consequently, encouraging clients with dementia to take on opportunities that enhance their optimism about living well with dementia may well enhance a person's ability to adjust to the condition.

3 *Disclosure and ownership.* A key element in helping a person to adjust to their dementia comes from encouraging them to be open in talking about the diagnosis. For many people a public ownership of their diagnosis also facilitates a different relationship with their dementia – one in which they are not defined by this, but rather have some control over it. One way to encourage

this process is for therapists to be curious about who within a client's social network knows about the dementia. For instance, during Session 5 of the Living Well with Dementia course (Cheston and Marshall, 2019) facilitators ask participants to indicate who they have told, what they have told them and whether there are people who have not been told but who still know. As I have outlined before in this book, finding creative ways to address issues around stigma can help people to work through some of the problematic elements of the diagnosis.

4 *Advocacy and peer support.* One of the most inspiring changes to occur within dementia care in recent years has been the growth of advocacy. Not only have individuals such as Keith Oliver, Hilary Doxford and Tommy Dunne talked openly about their experiences of living with dementia, but in the UK organizations like the DEEP[3] network are providing both peer support and a voice to insist that services should not be designed for people with dementia without actively involving them in this process.

5 *Encourage decision-making.* People living with dementia face a wide range of decisions, from ensuring there are appropriate financial controls in place, to reconciling themselves to being a car passenger rather than a driver, to allowing a continence pad to be changed. People need to make decisions about their medication and to plan for the future, including legal planning such as a making a will or setting in place advanced directives, such as legal power of attorney. More generally, people with dementia are faced on a daily basis with allowing themselves to become dependent on others – a process that involves trusting others to make decisions about their care. All of these decisions have the potential to raise intense emotions and therapists need to be sensitive to their expression and thoughtful in helping clients to process these.

Final words

Since the country's first national dementia strategy was established in 2009, dementia care in the UK has focused on finding ways to enable people to '*live well*' with their dementia. A central part of this strategy was to establish a sustainable system of early assessment and diagnosis in order to facilitate people living with dementia and their families to plan ahead and prepare for the future. Accordingly, providers within both the statutory and voluntary sector encourage people living with dementia to manage their illness by, for instance, creating a legal power of attorney or making financial decisions. Implicit within UK dementia services, then, is the belief that early assessment and diagnosis will facilitate further adjustment to dementia. Ironically, however, having identified the importance of adjustment, there has been little formal discussion

---

3 https://www.dementiavoices.org.uk/

of how dementia services can support this beyond the hope that it will follow on naturally from an early diagnosis.

For most people who are living with dementia, however, day-to-day life proceeds with awareness of the illness, if it exists at all, being pushed firmly into the background. Indeed, there is evidence that people who push their dementia away may also rate themselves as having a higher quality of life (Alexander et al., 2021). At the same time, being able to acknowledge and talk about their dementia does confer some advantages. As the husband of Anna, a woman who had attended a LivDem course described in Chapter 6 commented, '*Although [this] seems small it is very, very big. I mean once you've accepted you've got a problem then you will accept people trying to help you more. But if you're in denial that you have this problem then of course you're not prepared to accept help from anybody.*' It is the role of clinicians and psychotherapists to help people like Anna to both acknowledge their dementia and then to act on that knowledge.

Summary of Part 3: Becoming the same, but different

The Assimilation of Problematic Experiences model helps us to make sense of how people adjust to their dementia and how some people learn to live well with the condition, becoming less frightened and more accepting of it. This can be summarized as falling into three therapeutic tasks.

In the initial stages of adjustment people face a dilemma: whether to try to push the knowledge of dementia out of their mind (at the risk of losing control of some of their life) or to acknowledge and engage with the dementia (which is painful and distressing). The role of therapists is to help people to work their way through this ambivalence and to articulate both the problematic and dominant narratives. Often people with dementia explore these issues indirectly, for instance through stories and metaphors. In so doing, many people put a name to their problems without, at the same time, being emotionally overwhelmed.

The second therapeutic task involves finding distance from the distress. Therapists can support people in doing this by enabling them to make links between the past and the present and by encouraging them to think through who they tell about their dementia and what they tell them.

The third therapeutic task involves people integrating the knowledge of dementia into their identity and finding partial solutions for practical problems that they encounter. For therapists, helping people to work at this level may involve prompting clients to take decisions about their lives such as assigning a legal power of attorney, identifying healthy living skills or working out a 'bucket list' of goals to achieve.

Implications for people living with dementia

Many people living with dementia should think about the following points.

- Think about the choices they want to make around their dementia. On the one hand they may prefer not to look too closely into their dementia – and for many people it is possible to enjoy a good quality of life without acknowledging the existence of dementia. At the same time, however, people may feel that they need to make sense out of what is happening to them. Approaching dementia in this way enables people to stay in control of their life, but it can be emotionally painful.

- Recognize that adjusting to dementia involves addressing both the changes in themselves that have already occurred and additionally the prospect of future changes. They may not like the changes that they have seen in themselves. Indeed, they may well not like themselves much at times. However, it is possible to move through this and to come to terms with this new version of themselves.

- While many people are able to talk openly about their dementia without external support, finding someone who can provide time and space to think these issues over can often be very helpful.
- Over time, many people are able to talk about their dementia without feeling overwhelmed. One way to do this is to find some distance from the dementia and to realize that while it affects their life, it does not define them.

Implications for family carers

People who are caring for someone with dementia should think about the following points.

- Recognize signs about which particular therapeutic stage the person they are providing care for is working at. They may, for instance, be struggling to put a name to their dementia without feeling emotionally overwhelmed. Or they may be able to name the dementia but require help to distance themselves from this.
- Take advantage of situations where it may be possible to feel their way carefully and slowly into a conversation about dementia, while also giving the person they are caring for an opportunity to withdraw from this if necessary. Methods of bringing dementia into the conversation range from noticing moments where someone has mis-remembered a name, to flagging up a news story about Alzheimer's disease.
- Facilitate opportunities for the person with dementia to talk to others about their dementia, for instance through peer support groups.

Implications for therapists

Healthcare professionals whose job involves offering specific counselling or psychotherapy sessions should think about the following points.

- They should recognize that their client's neurological impairment and the erosion of their cognitive abilities does not inevitably mean that they cannot adjust to their dementia.
- They should identify the assimilation level that their clients are typically operating at and frame their therapeutic work accordingly.
- They should pace the intensity of their work at a level that their clients can sustain and allow them to oscillate between talking about, and withdrawing from, their dementia.
- They should offer opportunities for clients who seem to be managing their dementia well to 'check in' regularly, for instance through monthly or quarterly follow-up sessions.

Implications for dementia care workers

Staff working in dementia care should think about the following points.

- Recognize that for many people who are living with dementia, day-to-day life proceeds with an awareness of the illness being pushed firmly into the background. At the same time, it is important to identify opportunities within their service for people with dementia and their families to talk about their dementia.
- Support their clients in discussing their dementia, for instance by acknowledging both explicit and implicit references to the person having changed.
- Be curious with the people they work with as to how they are coping emotionally as well as practically with the knowledge of their dementia.

Part 4

Complicated psychotherapy

11 Neurological impairment and psychotherapy

The focus in the first three parts of this book has been on how helping people to talk about their dementia can facilitate those living with the disease to adjust to, and live well with, the condition. I have argued that having a conversation about the dementia is central to the psychotherapeutic process, regardless of the orientation of the therapist. Consequently, although I have touched on how psychotherapy can be adapted to accommodate a client's cognitive impairment, I have taken a position that cognitive impairment per se is not an obstacle or barrier to therapy taking place.

At the same time, however, I recognize that this cannot be an absolute position – and that inevitably the level and type of the neurological impairment that affects a person living with a dementia must be considered. In this chapter I will argue that even where people have very severe levels of cognitive impairment, adapted forms of psychotherapy can still play an important role within care. More specifically, even when formal psychotherapy sessions would be impractical, it may nevertheless be possible to use some psychotherapy skills informally, as is the case within resolution therapy (Stokes and Goudie, 1989, 1990). This is an issue that I will return to in Chapter 13 where I will explore the possibilities of *being* therapeutic as distinct from *doing* psychotherapy.

In this chapter I will set out how the type and severity of neurological impairment impacts on psychotherapy. Firstly, I will illustrate how the form of impairment can impede therapy by examining one specific diagnosis – that of frontotemporal dementia. Secondly, I will give a brief overview of how the global severity of impairment, regardless of any specific diagnosis inevitably impacts on a therapeutic process.

Frontotemporal dementia and psychotherapy

Frontotemporal dementia is, thankfully, a comparatively rare form of dementia. The term refers to damage arising from two separate but closely aligned areas of the brain – the frontal and the temporal lobes. The frontal areas of the two hemispheres of the brain (located behind the forehead and immediately above the eye socket) typically control or direct a person's behaviour – they enable us to think ahead, to plan our actions and importantly to understand the consequences of those actions, especially how they might seem to other people. The temporal lobes, on the other hand, typically those in the left-hand side of the brain for most people, relate to language – for instance by helping us to understand what others are saying, or enabling us to put our thoughts into words. While frontotemporal dementia, especially as the illness progresses, is likely to include damage to both lobes the diagnosis itself is often thought of as being composed of three different types, or variants, which I will describe below. Compared to someone with Alzheimer's disease, a person with any of these three variants of frontotemporal dementia may have relatively well-preserved short-term memory and the illness is more likely to come on at an earlier stage in life.

Behavioural-variant frontotemporal dementia

The symptoms associated with behavioural-variant frontotemporal dementia (or bv-FTD) typically include the person acting impulsively, sometimes in a sexually inappropriate way, being unsympathetic to, or apparently uncaring of, the impact of their behaviour on others, and not being able to plan their actions or to put these into a logical, thought-out sequence. As a clinical psychologist working within both community teams, and across in-patient wards and residential care units, I frequently came across people living with a dementia who would be described as having a frontotemporal version of dementia. Sometimes this diagnosis was based on detailed psychometric testing, careful observations, and the exclusion of other possible diagnoses, and evidenced by brain scans. In many cases, however, the diagnosis seemed to have been made prematurely, often as a way of explaining complex behaviours that were challenging for staff to respond to. On these occasions, the diagnosis seemed questionable to me and often prevented the service from looking at how the person's behaviour related to a range of underlying, and unmet, psychosocial needs (James and Jackman, 2017). However, just because a diagnosis of frontotemporal dementia is sometimes misapplied does not mean that the types of neurological deficit that it refers to are not all too real, and that they powerfully affect a person's ability to engage with the world around them.

My own experience of working with people with an established diagnosis of bv-FTD was that the nature of their cognitive impairment meant that the pre-requisites for therapeutic work were missing: the people I met struggled to mentalize – that is to say to they struggled to think about what was going on in either their own or another person's mind (Bateman and Fonagy, 2013). One of the abiding impressions I had of many of the people I worked with was that social interaction with other people was for them at best unnerving and at worst a cause of distress which they sought to avoid whenever possible. Consequently, my role as a clinical psychologist focused almost entirely on trying to understand the way in which the person's neurological impairment affected how they understood and interacted with the world around them. Together with the rest of the clinical team, I would work to structure the care around the person in a way that caused as little distress to them and to the people trying to provide care. Typically, this meant framing the person's challenging behaviour within a psychological framework (e.g., Jackman and Beatty, 2015; James and Jackman, 2017), and working with members of the family – much as I outlined in Chapter 5.

Primary progressive aphasia

Primary progressive aphasia (or PPA) involves changes in a person's ability to use language (aphasia) as the person speaks slowly, struggles to articulate their thoughts, especially in complex sentences, gets words in the wrong order, or uses words incorrectly. In addition to these difficulties in using language to express themselves, someone with PPA may also have problems in understanding what other people say to them, which is known as receptive aphasia. PPA normally comes on in midlife, before age 65, but can occur in late life as well. PPA is itself comprised of three different types, which are distinguished by the kind of language problems that appear first.

In the semantic variant of PPA, people slowly lose the ability to understand individual words in a spoken sentence. Sometimes they also begin to lose the ability to recognize faces and common objects. In non-fluent or agrammatic PPA, a person's speaking is very laboured and without grammatical structure, such that they may leave out linking words (such as 'to', 'and', 'from'). In logopenic PPA, a person can understand words and sentences that are said to them and does not have problems with grammar but struggles to find the right words to use during a conversation.

When I have worked psychotherapeutically with people with PPA or other forms of dementia that limit communication, I have tried to create a context in which the client has the time and space both to express themselves and to understand the therapist's comments. In these cases, the focus of therapy has largely been on the difficulties that these problems around communication create. This process is illustrated in the case of Carrie in this chapter.

Movement disorders

Some rare neurological movement disorders are associated with FTD, including corticobasal syndrome, progressive supranuclear palsy and amyotrophic lateral sclerosis (sometimes known as Lou Gehrig's disease). All three of these illnesses produce changes in muscle or motor functions either with or without changes in the person's behaviour or language. Corticobasal syndrome, which causes arms and legs to become uncoordinated or stiff, typically begins at around the age of 60. Progressive supranuclear palsy causes difficulty in walking and changes in posture as well as affecting a person's balance and ability to walk. Amyotrophic lateral sclerosis is a motor neuron disease and causes muscle weakness or wasting.

Carrie: Providing a containing place to talk about not talking

Carrie was referred to me for post-diagnostic counselling after she had received a diagnosis of Logopenic Progressive Aphasia. LPA is a type of Primary Progressive Aphasia – typically caused by damage to the temporal areas of the left hemisphere of the brain. While the person is able to articulate grammatically correct sentences, and to understand simple sentences, their speech is slow and hesitant and they are likely to have trouble understanding long or complex verbal information. Carrie scored at quite a low level on a general assessment of her cognitive abilities (48 out of a possible 100 on the revised Addenbrooke's Cognitive Examination) but this was partly due to her difficulties in communicating answers coherently, rather than reflecting an inability to formulate a response at all.

When I met Carrie for the first time, she was accompanied by Charlotte, her close friend. Carrie was widowed, and her children lived in Manchester, a two-hour journey or more from her. While Charlotte's presence seemed to be partly to provide emotional support, there were also practical reasons why Carrie asked for her to be present; she sometimes asked Charlotte to clarify what she was trying to say. Carrie had a strong and supportive set of friends locally and had also been referred to a speech and language therapist, which she had found helpful.

In terms of the assimilation model, Carrie seemed to me to be working at Level 5 or 6. She used the word 'dementia' spontaneously and she seemed to be emotionally connected to her loss, clearly being touched by the sadness of her diagnosis. Carrie also spoke about how she coped with her dementia both by using the communication strategies that her speech therapist had recommended and also by simplifying her life. She had, for instance, started to cook simpler meals and was using adaptations in her house, such as a cradle to enable her to pour hot water from the kettle. In talking over how Carrie had adjusted to the diagnosis with them both, we agreed that she was managing well and that there was no obvious reason to enter into an extended contract of psychological work at that time. I therefore did not offer her another session, but we agreed that should her situation change then she could get back in touch with me.

Six months later, Carrie's memory clinic doctor contacted me again to ask if I would offer her another appointment. When we met again, she still seemed to be socially active and had now started to tell her friends that she had dementia. Carrie managed to find ways of accommodating her language difficulties by speaking slowly and deliberately. However, she was aware of changes within herself, which was why she had asked to be re-referred. Carrie told me that she felt diminished by her dementia, although she also had a strong sense of being the same person that she had always been. This diminishment sat heavily on her and in particular she felt ashamed at how much she relied not just on Charlotte but on her other friends. She was also frightened about the future – she knew perfectly well that her hold on her life as she had lived it for many years was becoming more precarious, and the emotional impact of these changes was understandably disturbing for her.

We agreed to continue to meet – initially once every three months, but with the understanding that this may need to become more frequent in time. The aim of meeting together would be to provide her with a space to think about the impact of her dementia on her life.

In our next sessions, I continued to be impressed by how well Carrie was coping with her dementia. She felt that although her ability to communicate had become worse, she was still finding ways to express herself. She had invited a group of friends around for lunch, and she had been pleased with how well she had done and how she had coped with problems as they emerged. This relieved her of some of her guilt around her dementia – it allowed her to have a sense of giving as well as receiving from her friends. Carrie and Charlotte also told me that she had been able to ask her children to be a little more present in her life as she needed their support.

As we continued to meet, so Carrie's word-finding difficulties deteriorated and it required a concerted effort for her to verbalize her thoughts. Carrie remained determined to live her life as normally as she could, going to the theatre and cinema, and carrying a card with her which she could pass to people if necessary to explain that she had a form of dementia that affected her ability to talk.

Carrie gradually became concerned about another problem that her dementia was causing her: she had begun to find it hard to estimate distances, and as a consequence, was increasingly unsure of walking, especially down steps when the lighting was poor. Recently, she had fallen at the cinema, and she was now also worried that she might fall at home. Consequently, she had signed up for a scheme where she wore an alarm around her neck which she could pull if she fell and needed to alert someone to help her.

This solution was only a partial one however – there were other risks about living at home, particularly when she was cooking or making a hot drink for herself. Carrie had also now given up reading altogether. Her scores on cognitive assessments deteriorated markedly and she was conscious of taking longer and longer to complete her sentences. Carrie compensated for this by talking around the subject and increasingly looking to Charlotte to interpret for her in our sessions. At this point, however, neither of them felt that Carrie's level of dependency was severe enough that it would be worthwhile having an external care agency involved.

As life was becoming increasingly difficult for Carrie, we arranged to meet more frequently. She became increasingly distressed at her loss of ability to judge depth, alternating within sessions between crying for her losses and pushing the significance of this emerging threat away and minimizing its impact. I was also contacted outside the meetings by both Charlotte and by Carrie's children, all of whom were concerned about the risks that she faced. However, they did not feel able to express their concerns to her as they feared such an emotive subject would overwhelm her communication skills. In order to resolve these tensions, I asked Carrie's permission to invite her children to our next session.

This was a difficult session for Carrie. In our work together she had been clear that she saw accepting help within her house as a marker of the frailty that she dreaded. Both Charlotte and her family were able to use the therapeutic space to share their fears with her – and she was able to express her distress and to be listened to. As a compromise, together they agreed for her to be assessed by an occupational therapist to identify what level of support, if any, she might need, and that she would have the final word on how she should be supported.

Our next session turned out to be the final time that I met Carrie in person. Through Charlotte, she told me that while there had been many tears, she was now resolved that she would need a much-enhanced care package with a live-in paid carer. Although there were some teething problems in setting this up, she and Charlotte were optimistic that they could find a good balance between support and independence. Our further meetings were disrupted by the Covid-19 pandemic and my own illness. My next contact with Carrie was through a telephone call – a medium which Carrie understandably loathed and which she would only tolerate because Charlotte was part of her support bubble and could therefore be available to interpret her answers. The solution that had emerged was that Carrie now had a '*lovely lady with her all the time*' and that '*all [was] going well*'.

Psychotherapy with people with severe levels of cognitive impairment

Over time, so the neurological impairments caused by Alzheimer's disease and other causes of dementia spread and become more intense. As this occurs, a person's ability to identify, acknowledge and make sense of their emotions is reduced. Similarly, increasing difficulties in retaining information and in articulating, communicating and verbalizing their thoughts all progressively impede a person's ability to make sense out of what is happening to them. It also restricts their ability to take part in what we might describe as 'formal' therapy – that part of psychotherapeutic work that involves meeting at a regular time, in a consistent setting to work on an agreed area of that person's life.

However, this does not mean that more severe cognitive impairments put an end to a clinician using psychotherapeutic skills. It may, for instance, be possible to use some psychotherapeutic skills – especially the core person-centred counselling skills of empathic listening, unconditional positive regard and congruence – within the context of an 'informal' psychotherapeutic engagement. The relevance of these skills throughout the dementia journey is underlined by the fact that some people who have relatively high levels of neurological impairment can, under the right circumstances, describe complex aspects of their life circumstances. Linda Clare and her colleagues (Clare et al., 2008a, 2008b), for instance, have argued that nearly two-thirds of the people that they interviewed were able to demonstrate thoughtful consideration of an aspect of their situation and the implications that this carried, such as being brought to live in a residential home, losing their spouse or reflecting on their experience of dying. This capacity for reflection also seems to be true, for at least some people, even where there are more severe levels of neurological impairment. Thus, Beatrice Goodwin and Hilary Waters interviewed 12 people with advanced dementia living in hospital wards, nursing homes, or a hospice (Goodwin and Waters, 2009). Despite their advanced dementia, the people in Beatrice and Hilary's study appeared to have, and were able to express, views on the care they wanted at the end of life. Moreover, the authors reported that there was some evidence to suggest that for some participants their views may have evolved since they were diagnosed, including a greater acceptance of death.

Moreover, the emotional load caused by dementia is not eliminated by these neurological impairments – indeed it is likely that the cognitive changes both act as an increased emotional threat and impair those psychological defences that the person previously relied on to maintain an emotional equilibrium. The reduced ability of people with severe levels of dementia to process their emotions cognitively, and to express them in words, means that they are more likely to express them in another way – for instance through their behaviour.

Anyone who has walked through a hospital ward or care home and witnessed the distress that is symptomatic of what Kitwood referred to as 'unattended' dementia will be able to locate in that experience the collapse of defences and the *'invasion of rage, grief and fear'* (Kitwood, 1997; Kitwood and Brooker, 2019). Emotions are everywhere in the care of people with severe levels of dementia. We see the presence of unattended emotional distress in the behaviour of, for example: the woman who compulsively writes down her name as she is afraid that she will forget who she is; the farmer who dresses for work at 4.00 a.m. every day; the man who scribbles down everything that happens to him in a series of makeshift diaries that he then frantically refers back to in order to reassure himself that he can live with his memory failures. Emotion is ever present in the lives of people living with dementia.

Psychological models of the behaviour of people with severe levels of cognitive impairment arising from their dementia (often referred to as 'distressed' or 'challenging' behaviour) frame these behaviours as potential communications of a person's emotions (Moniz-Cook et al., 2003; Salzman et al., 2008; Stokes, 2017; James and Jackman, 2017). This person-centred approach to challenging behaviour focuses on the importance of understanding the origins of this behaviour and places this within the broader context of human needs. People with dementia have the same human needs as everyone else. Indeed, the need for emotional security and stability is likely to be especially pronounced for people with dementia. Challenging behaviour often occurs when a person attempts to meet their needs in an inappropriate way.

It is beyond the scope of this book to explore psychological models of challenging behaviour in any depth, but what is relevant is the way in which these often reflect an emotional response to the world around the person – responses which suggest the need for an 'informal' form of psychotherapeutic engagement. As Steven Sabat (personal communication) has suggested, challenging behaviour can often be triggered by a person's extreme reaction to their dementia.

One way to illustrate how the behaviours of people with more severe levels of dementia may reflect emotional responses to the world around them is to look at what is often referred to as agitation – that is a range of behaviours that include verbal and physical acts of aggression such as hitting or screaming, non-aggressive acts of distress, such as pacing or repetitive behaviour and verbal signs of distress such as shouting or crying (Cohen-Mansfield, 1997). A series of studies by the American psychologist Jiska Cohen-Mansfield and her colleagues into the psychological origins of the behaviour of nursing-home residents with very severe levels of cognitive impairment suggested that there were four different patterns of agitated behaviour – each of which reflected an emotional response to different aspects of their care (e.g., Rabinowitz et al., 2005; Salzman et al., 2008). For instance, residents who were in pain and depressed or lonely were likely to express their distress verbally and in an agitated manner. Other residents who were generally in good health but had a degree of sensory loss and, without meaningful activities to take part in, seemed to gain some stimulation from walking around the nursing home. Finally, some men were more likely to be physically aggressive, especially when the environment was cold or noisy, or if they felt threatened, for instance when a member of staff tried to provide them with personal care.

All of these different behavioural expressions of distress reflect very human needs – for instance the need to be loved, or to have a meaningful role that provides self-esteem, to have social contact or to have stimulating and meaningful activities to take part in. Importantly, as part of good dementia care, those around the person with dementia need to be able to draw on 'informal' psychotherapy skills, including an empathic response to the needs that underlie these behaviours.

Informal therapy

Resolution therapy

Resolution therapy is based on the proposition that while people with dementia may be losing their cognitive abilities, their capacity to experience and feel as human beings is largely unaffected (Bush, 2003). This is an informal counselling approach that draws on person-centred counselling principles and was developed specifically for work with people with dementia by Graham Stokes and Fiona Goudie (e.g., Stokes and Goudie, 1989, 1990). Resolution therapy views challenging behaviour as containing a hidden emotional message. They contend that the most appropriate response to this behaviour is for family and paid carers to sensitively reflect the underlying causes of a person's distress back to them, empathizing with the concealed meanings and feelings (Morton, 1999, 2017). For instance, when trying to comfort a new resident in a residential care home who is trying to find a small child that she maintains is lost, a carer might suspect that this behaviour reflects a partially disguised expression of insecurity arising from the impact of cognitive deterioration, aggravated by the recent admission (Miesen, 1992, 2016; Magai and Cohen, 1998). The carer might then tentatively offer a response along the lines of '*It's really upsetting to feel lost. Sometimes it can be difficult when you move somewhere new*'. This disguised and indirect way of expressing emotions is, of course, very similar to the way in which problematic material related to dementia might be explored in the early stages of the assimilation model, and which was set out in Chapter 8.

Reflecting the person's feelings back to them in this way enables them to make sense of their behaviour and, in this way, the person with dementia and their family can begin to talk about, and ultimately manage, these underlying feelings. There is strong anecdotal evidence that resolution therapy can be an important part of the care plans implemented by nurses, healthcare assistants and other paid carers in daily contact with people living with dementia (Bush, 2003). It is certainly a way of working that I routinely taught to care staff and asked them to use as part of their response to the distress of their clients or residents (Bush, 2003). In this way, person-centred counselling in the form of resolution therapy and good listening skills form an essential part of a therapeutic repertoire, alongside a range of other options for addressing the person's emotional needs, such as introducing transitional objects (Stephens et al., 2013) such as dolls (James et al., 2006) or by playing the voice of their family carer (Evans et al., 2015).

Validation therapy

Validation therapy or VT was developed by Naomi Feil (Feil, 1993, 1996) for older people with cognitive impairments. Initially, Feil intended VT to be used with people she described as being the 'disoriented old-old' (Babins, 1988), but the approach was subsequently broadened to include work with people who have a diagnosis of dementia. Although a range of different psychological ideas have been incorporated into VT, Feil suggested that confusion and disorientation were the product of the person withdrawing into the past in an attempt to resolve unfinished past conflicts. Feil's approach to therapy was therefore based on the general principle of validation – the acceptance of the reality and personal truth of another's experience (Neal and Wright, 2003). The goal of a validation therapist is to enter imaginatively into the feelings and perceptions of the person and to acknowledge the emotion that lies behind their words and actions. The principles of VT can be used as the basis of both formal therapy groups and also as an informal adjunct to good dementia care practice and it incorporates a range of recognized psychotherapy and counselling techniques, such as empathic listening (Feil, 1993; Neal and Wright, 2003).

While VT has attracted some criticism from researchers, who dispute the underlying premise that disoriented behaviour reflects a failure to resolve a previous life stage (e.g., Cheston and Bender, 1999), Feil's work was the first significant attempt to incorporate psychotherapeutic principles into dementia care, and as such it has been influential. Indeed, VT has been the subject of a range of research, including two randomized studies (Deponte and Missan, 2007; Toseland et al., 1997). Unusually for psychotherapy research in this area, both of these studies were set in long-term care facilities and included partici-pants whose levels of cognitive functioning was relatively low. The results from both studies were, however, inconclusive (Cheston and Ivanecka, 2017): Deponte and Missan found decreased behavioural distress in the VT arm, although a control intervention (reminiscence therapy) led to improved cogni-tive functioning. Toseland et al., (1997) found lowered levels of verbal and physical aggression in the VT group, but nursing staff reported that partici-pants' levels of aggression improved more in the control groups. Taking the research into VT as a whole, a Cochrane review (which is internationally recog-nized as the most authoritative type of systematic review of evidence in an area) concluded that there was insufficient evidence to allow any conclusion about the efficacy of validation therapy for people with either dementia or a cognitive impairment (Neal and Wright, 2003).

Final words

Psychotherapy places considerable demands on clients. This is especially true for clients who are facing the profound psychological threat of dementia while living with the immediate consequences of a reduced cognitive capacity. Keith Oliver, for instance, reports that he comes away from his sessions feeling drained and emotionally dysregulated (Oliver, personal communication). Con-sequently, therapists have largely focused their efforts on people who have received their diagnosis relatively recently, and who have a mild or moderate level of impairment resulting from Alzheimer's disease, vascular dementia or a combination of these.

Nevertheless, therapeutic approaches can be modified to accommodate both the type of impairment and its more severe forms. While I have argued that some people with a diagnosis of bv-FTD are unlikely to be able to benefit from therapy, the communication limitations caused by other forms of fronto-temporal dementia are not necessarily barriers to participation. Indeed, even when it is inappropriate to deliver psychotherapy formally within specific ses-sions, it may nevertheless be possible to use some counselling skills informally for instance through resolution therapy. More generally, two crucial elements of psychotherapy – the need for an empathic, imaginative response to distress, and the capacity to build a relationship in which people feel secure and valued – which are essentially psychotherapeutic skills, are at the heart of good dementia care, no matter what a person's cognitive level. This is an issue I will return to in Chapter 13 where I will explore the possibilities of *being* ther-apeutic as distinct from *doing* psychotherapy.

12 Working with social and personal fragility

If an aim of psychotherapy is to enable people to change in some way, then potential clients need to have the capacity to be open to the possibility of change. In the last chapter I set out how the neurological impairments associated with dementia can act as a barrier to change and thus impede psychotherapy. In this chapter I will look at how social and personal factors may also prevent a person with dementia being open to the possibility of change.

Social circumstances may become a barrier to change if the person lacks the resources to support a new emerging reality – for instance if they live on their own, or within a relationship which either does not support or even actively discourages change. Personal factors may also act to impede change if the person's sense of themselves is too fragile – for instance if they are bound up in extrinsic markers of status, or if their psychological defences are too entrenched to permit them to acknowledge existential threat. One such personality pattern is that of narcissism – when a high apparent level of explicit self-esteem masks a fragile, implicit lack of self-esteem. Consequently, people who are highly narcissistic are unable to tolerate the emotional dysregulation that is intrinsic to the losses and threats surrounding dementia.

Social factors: Living alone

Of the estimated 900,000 people in the UK who are thought to be living with dementia, roughly 120,000, or one person in every seven lives on their own (Alzheimer's Society, 2019). Just as this presents different practical challenges, so it also represents a different set of psychological challenges: whereas someone who is living with a partner may be able to fall back on a relationship established perhaps over decades of mutual support and interdependency, the person who is living on their own is forced by necessity to be self-reliant. Consequently, as the progressive nature of dementia forces the single person to become more dependent on external support so this can present a more obvious challenge to their identity than that faced within many couples. Whereas within a couple, issues around dependency can often be somewhat blurred as the person's partner gradually acquires more responsibility, and may acquiesce in preserving an illusion of competence, no such ambiguity is available for the single person. They are either able to support themselves independently or they are not able to do so and require external support if they are to continue to live in the community.

The threat to identity provoked by dementia is therefore often much starker when someone lives on their own than when they are in a co-habiting relationship. In my experience of working with people who were living on their own with dementia, I was sometimes aware that acknowledging change was a leap too far for some people and that they preferred to find a way to ignore the dementia and to retreat into well-established routines often supported by children or friends. The presence of a therapist, then, in itself represents a threat to identity in the sense that it implies the person requires support. Consequently, I often found it difficult to establish the basis for a therapeutic relationship, with potential clients either withdrawing from this work, or not being willing to take up the offer in the first place. In these circumstances, clinicians may still make use of their psychotherapeutic skills – but indirectly through supporting the extended family rather than directly working with the person with dementia.

Social factors: Dysfunctional responses to dementia

There has long been a recognition in dementia research that the ability of individuals to acknowledge their dementia is connected to social factors. Tom Kitwood (1997), for instance, suggested that levels of insight of residents in a nursing home would be a reliable index for the quality of the care provided within that home: in other words, malignant social psychological environments would be associated with low levels of well-being and a lack of insight. While Kitwood focused on personhood, other explorations of identity in the dementia care literature continue to echo the self as inherently social in nature. Steven Sabat (Sabat, 2002; Sabat et al., 2004), for instance, describes the self as containing three related concepts, all of which are enacted in the social world. Crucial to Sabat's representation of self is the idea that people will position themselves within a social interaction by presenting a version of themselves that maintains their self-esteem. Importantly if, during a social interaction, a person believes that they are being positioned in a way that undermines their self-esteem, then they will respond by seeking to reposition themselves in a more positive way. While Sabat's work has often been explored within institutions or other areas of dementia care, it also relates to the positions that marital partners seek to create for themselves within relationships as the example of Jane and Henry below illustrates.

As I outlined in Parts 1 and 2, the role of the partner of the person with dementia is central to any psychotherapeutic process. Not just are there practical issues, for instance around prompting the person to remember an appointment, but partners also crucially provide emotional support and reassurance. There is also some evidence that the quality of a couple's relationship at diagnosis is linked with outcomes such as the likelihood of challenging behaviour later on (Edwards et al., 2018). One way in which a poor marital relationship can lead to a problematic outcome and make it difficult to engage in a therapeutic relationship can be if the person living with dementia feels that if they acknowledge any lapses then this would create tension within the relationship. My attempt to work with Jane and Henry illustrates this point.

Jane and Henry

Jane and Henry had been married for 35 years before Jane developed Alzheimer's disease at the age of 66. Henry was a retired engineer, who had spent all of his professional life working for a large motor manufacturer and his work had meant that he had spent long periods away from home. Jane had worked as a primary school teacher and had brought up their two children with relatively little support from her husband or from other members of her family. Henry had retired at the age of 60, and three years after this Jane had been diagnosed with Alzheimer's disease.

When I met them, Jane emphasized that little, if anything was wrong with her – statements that Henry clearly disagreed with. Jane, for her part, especially resented Henry's attempts to help her and on a number of occasions they had had heated arguments. These seemed to have been triggered by Henry offering Jane advice when she was preparing a meal. When I discussed these incidents with them, Henry would correct Jane if she made a mistake in her recollection of what had happened. When I asked him how Jane might feel to have her memory challenged in this way, he focused on the importance of providing a factually accurate narrative and showed little empathic understanding of how being corrected might impact his wife.

When I asked the couple to tell me about the events that had led up to the most recent row, Jane described how Henry had corrected her when she was cooking the Sunday roast – advice that she resented. For his part, Henry seemed oblivious to the possibility that his prompting might have been experienced by Jane as an intrusion into an important part of her identity. Instead, he emphasized that she needed his help and compared his providing advice to similar situations where he had coached a much more junior engineer through a tricky mechanical problem – a comparison which further upset Jane as she felt that it suggested that she was an apprentice to his supervisor.

Within our sessions, as Henry continued to insist that his wife needed his direction, so Jane retreated within herself and further away from acknowledging that she experienced any problems. This, in turn, pushed Henry to be more insistent that she could not manage, and so the interpersonal cycle continued with increasing strains and distress apparent for both of them.

My work with Henry and Jane spanned only two sessions. The appointment for the third session was cancelled as a crisis had developed. In an argument, again related to cooking, Jane had thrown saucepans at her husband, and he had called the police, who in turn called the duty social worker and psychiatrist. They responded by admitting Jane to a psychiatric hospital. Here, Jane's condition deteriorated even further, and Henry refused to have her discharged home, insisting instead that she enter residential care.

In retrospect, I have wondered whether if I had been able to engage Jane and Henry in a more directive form of work that focused on their interpersonal interactions, such as Balfour's Living Together with Dementia programme, then this might have helped them to address the conflicting patterns of interaction around her dependency. However, I am unsure whether Henry's lack of empathy and his blunt problem-solving responses to his wife's impairments would have rendered even this approach ineffective.

The example of Jane and Henry illustrates what can happen when those around the person with dementia position them as incompetent in some way, thus reducing their social identity (Sabat, 2002, 2018). However, it is also the case that some social relationships can resist any form of change – and instead position the person with dementia in a social role that no longer fits them. This can happen, for instance, where families maintain that the person's dementia is not real – either from a fear that the person will disintegrate if they are forced to confront their illness, or because they themselves cannot bear the thought that change is necessary. These social forces often become apparent within memory clinics, as families request that the person being assessed for dementia is not told about their diagnosis. This is not only ethically challenging, but in seeking to eliminate all discussion of dementia, this silence may also jeopardize any opportunity for adjustment. At the same time there are instances where individuals may be too emotionally fragile to tolerate any discussion of their dementia, and it is to this topic that I will now turn.

Personal resilience and fragility

The capacity of human beings to assimilate problematic experiences such as dementia depends not only on the social world around them, but also on a number of internal or personal factors. The person with dementia needs to hold onto the fact that they are neither completely changed, nor quite the same person – rather that they are the same but different. It involves them coming to a position where they can feel that, despite the dementia, they are still of value, that they continue to love others and to be loved themselves. In other words, adjusting to dementia depends on someone having a level of personal resilience (Windle, 2011).

Psychology is replete with different ways of defining and understanding what determines whether people are psychologically resilient or fragile. One way of representing this that I have found useful comes from terror management theory or TMT (e.g., Solomon et al., 1991). TMT holds that the difference between individuals in the way in which they react to reminders of their own death or illness is related to a range of psychological resources including self-esteem (see Chapters 2 and 3). Thus, when people with higher levels of self-esteem are reminded of their own mortality, they are less likely than people with lower levels of self-esteem to respond defensively or to become anxious. This model is clearly potentially important to dementia care – it suggests that people may be more able to tolerate being reminded of their dementia if they have higher levels of self-esteem. Conversely, people with a lower level of psychological resources, including self-esteem, may be less able to be reminded of their dementia without becoming anxious. As I have described above, together with colleagues, I was able to show that temporarily increasing psychological resources, including self-esteem, enabled people living with dementia to recall more information about their dementia without at the same time increasing their anxiety (Ismail et al., 2018). This applied both to the most threatening aspects of dementia (such as forgetting the names of loved ones) and to the less-threatening facets (e.g., that some forms of dementia can be caused by a build-up of proteins in the brain).

From this basis, we can conjecture that people with dementia with low levels of self-esteem may be less able to think about their illness and especially its more threatening aspects than are those people with higher levels of self-esteem. However, this begs the question of what exactly constitutes either high or low levels of self-esteem. At one level, this is quite a simple question to answer: it may be easy to picture someone who seems to have a good level of self-esteem. They seem to be confident and self-assured but without having to remind people of their own achievements. Similarly, people with low levels of self-esteem may also be quite easy to recognize. They may lack confidence and be nervous in social situations. However, when we explore this more deeply it can be complicated. Thus, one important distinction is between implicit and explicit self-esteem. One way of thinking about implicit self-esteem is that it refers to a person's unconscious self-evaluations – whether they feel good about themselves on the inside, if you like. By contrast, explicit self-esteem relates to conscious displays of self-worth – people who need to remind others of their importance and status, but where this is not necessarily a valid reflection of how they actually feel about themselves (Bosson et al., 2008).

Research suggests that implicit and explicit self-esteem assess two distinct underlying processes and are often uncorrelated or only weakly correlated (Di Pierro et al., 2016). Importantly, it is possible for people to display both high explicit self-esteem, and yet have low levels of implicit self-esteem – and this seems to be part of the make-up of people with narcissistic tendencies.

Narcissism in people with dementia

Narcissism is typically referred to as existing on a spectrum or continuum, ranging from people who display a few narcissistic traits, to others who would meet the diagnostic criteria for a narcissistic personality disorder (McBride, 2008). People with narcissistic tendencies oscillate between states of high, often, grandiose levels of explicit self-esteem, and fragile states of dysregulated affect in which their interior or implicit self is experienced as empty (Horowitz, 1989; Young and Flanagan, 1998; Dimaggio et al., 2002). Consequently, people with narcissistic traits have a need for admiration or validation as well as a deep sense of entitlement, even though their achievements do not merit this. At the same time, however, they are likely to be unable to deal with criticism, and instead their own hidden feelings of insecurity and shame are projected into others. Consequently, people with narcissistic traits are themselves highly critical of others, and attack those people who challenge or undermine their external self.

For people with a pre-morbid predisposition to narcissism who develop an illness causing dementia, the increasing difficulties in carrying out the many different tasks that are part and parcel of everyday living may present specific challenges (Cheston, 2021). In particular, these may be experienced in terms of a loss of control over not only their cognitive functioning, but also in terms of a changing relationship with the social world. To admit to no longer being able to carry out a simple task because of the diminishment of dementia is likely to be intolerable because such failures threaten the person's heightened sense of their own self-worth. Similarly, to acknowledge the diagnosis of dementia would threaten the fragile nature of their self-concept. Instead, someone with narcissistic tendencies may react by flattering, intimidating or otherwise trying to control others who represent a threat to their fragile, implicit self-esteem. Where this is not successful, then they may respond with intense rage.

In many cases where someone with dementia has a pre-morbid narcissistic personality, then attempting to work psychotherapeutically with them may not be advisable as any attempt to engage them in thinking around their illness may be too threatening. At the same time, however, it may still be possible to work in the system around the person to support them in providing care. Typically, within dementia care, the advice given to relatives frames the responses of an individual to their dementia within a neurological, rather than a psychotherapeutic context. Thus, it is not uncommon for all of the person's behaviour to be attributed to the underlying illness rather than to ways of responding to threat that have been present for most of the person's lifetime. Psychotherapeutic skills are important, not just because they enable a clinician to engage more effectively with the family carer's own sadness and distress, but because they can help carers to understand the dynamic nature of their relationship and thus find a way forward.

I will now look at a case example of working with a woman who was providing care to her husband who had strong narcissistic traits, to illustrate the potential impact of supportive psychotherapy in enhancing resilience within a relationship.

James and Muriel: Working indirectly with narcissism

James was a 75-year-old man who was referred to me after he had attended a memory clinic. During the assessment process he had been dismissive and sarcastic, and when he was offered feedback by the team about how he had fared in the assessment, he had belittled the assessment process and angrily left the clinic before he could be given the diagnosis.

I was asked by the team to meet James as his adult children had raised concerns about not only what they perceived as a declining memory but also because they were concerned about how he behaved towards their mother, Muriel. When I met James in an out-patient clinic, he insisted that there was nothing wrong with him, and that the assessment results were an aberration. He was clear that he saw no need to meet me, and that he was only attending the appointment to please his children. Our session was therefore shorter than usual and ended with a compromise agreement that I would visit him at home so that I could find out more about his family's concerns for him.

When I visited James at his home, he refused to see me and told me instead to speak with Muriel, who he insisted was the one who had the problem. I asked Muriel what she made of her husband's memory, and she told me of his repeated mistakes around, for instance, shopping, paying bills, or driving and how he would angrily blame her whenever things went wrong for him. She told me that the referral had been precipitated because he had left the local newsagents with a newspaper that he had not paid for. When the shop owner that he had known for many years had asked him for payment this had led to an argument, which ended when the shop owner threatened to report James to the police if he did this again.

Muriel felt that James was coping with his poor memory in just the same way that he had responded to anything that displeased him throughout his life – by pretending that it did not exist and by reacting angrily if he was challenged. She gave me an example of how, when their children had been younger, they had lived in Central America, and would occasionally have to secure the house when it was threatened by a tropical storm. During a particularly awful storm, James had become frightened that the roof would blow off the house, and he had hidden in a small cupboard. Later, he threatened her and their children with a machete, saying that he would kill them if they told anyone about what he had done.

Muriel also told me that, recently, when James had been frustrated by his cognitive impairment, he had punched and slapped her and on one occasion had held a knife against her throat. She had also found handwritten notes hidden in his bedroom in which James bitterly blamed members of his family for stealing from him and accusing them of plotting to get rid of him. For Muriel, James's denial of dementia seemed to be one more way in which he pushed away those parts of his life that he could not tolerate.

Whenever I visited, James would make a joke about whether I had come to take him to the '*loony bin*', or whether he could be prescribed a holiday in his childhood home in South Africa. He would then dismiss me and vanish upstairs.

As working directly with James was not possible, I instead met Muriel regularly to talk about the implications of her decision to keep living and caring for a man who not only abused her, but also refused to acknowledge that he needed care. While making sure that I followed our service's procedures to safeguard those people who were at risk of violence from their partner, my discussions with Muriel focused on making sense of James's behaviour by framing this as a continuation of underlying narcissistic tendencies. In this way, Muriel was able to consider different ways of minimizing the risk of James's explosive rage while maintaining a reasonable standard of life for herself.

During our work together Muriel took up the metaphor of a narcissistic bubble to describe her delicate balancing act around James – he was, she said, living in his own bubble: when the bubble was intact, then James could be outwardly affable and charming. While inside the bubble, he lived in a fantasy world. But the bubble was fragile and could be easily pierced by reality, and when it did burst, James reacted to even small threats to his self-esteem by blaming and attacking those around him either physically or verbally. Muriel saw her role as protecting the bubble from being punctured, and repairing any small leaks that developed. She took the conscious decision to flatter him at these times, playing the part of admirer to his admired personae, laughing with him at his jokes and idiosyncrasies.

At the same time, our meetings helped Muriel to find a way to hold onto the world as it really was, not as James would have it to be. She started singing in the church choir and worked around James's objections to tidy up the accumulation of 20 years of hoarding newspapers and magazines in their spare bedroom (a room that he had previously kept locked) so that visitors could stay overnight and allow her to have a break.

In effect, James and Muriel found a manner of living together in which both of them avoided situations in which he would feel undermined or slighted. Thus, Muriel took care to avoid confronting James with what he could not do, and he retreated more and more into his dreams of going on safari. With this, and many other steps, Muriel found a way to care for James without pricking his narcissistic bubble and at the same time began to reclaim her life away from his domination.

I continued to see Muriel every few months until James became ill with a heart condition and was admitted to hospital.

Final words

It is important that clinicians assess the capacity of a person to adapt to their dementia before deciding whether, and if so, how to offer psychotherapy. This assessment needs to cover not only the level and nature of the person's cognitive impairment, but also the social and personal resources available to them. In assessing the availability of social resources, therapists need to be mindful of the person's living circumstances, and the way in which the person is positioned by others and positions themselves in relationship to their dementia. Where the personal resources available to people are thin, as is the case for those people who habitually fall back on narcissistic defences, it may not be possible to work directly with the person living with dementia. Nevertheless it may be possible to sustain their care by working indirectly through the wider care system and building a sustainable discourse based around psychotherapeutic as well as neurological principles.

13 Doing therapy and being therapeutic

> 'Since this paper is entitled "Psychotherapy and Dementia", I would like now to clear up one possible misunderstanding. I have not been outlining a new kind of psychotherapy, specifically for those who are undergoing a dementing illness; nor have I been implying that it would be desirable for a new brand of specialist – the "dementia psychotherapist" to emerge. My suggestion is, rather, that our whole approach to caregiving in dementia needs to be informed by insights that derive from psychotherapy. It is here, moreover, that we can find a satisfying rationale for the excellent work that many people are already doing. This work, I would describe as "therapeutic care".'
>
> Tom Kitwood (1990), p 55.

The title of this book, and this book series, reference Tom Kitwood's definitive 1997 account of person-centred care: *Dementia Reconsidered.* Now, Tom was not a psychotherapist, even if he was in this area, as in so many others, remarkably well-read. So when, in 1990, he published a paper in the newsletter of the British Psychological Society's Psychotherapy Section, he did so with at least half an eye on the wider applications of psychotherapy for dementia care. The main point for him in writing this paper seems to have been not so much to argue the case for psychotherapists and counsellors to offer therapy to people with dementia (although he clearly believes that it would be good to do so), but rather to argue the case that good dementia care was inherently based on psychotherapeutic principles, even if the practitioners concerned did not realize that this was what they were doing. As he states: *'I acknowledge with admiration the best dementia caregiving that I know, both in the NHS and in the private sector. People who do this work, day after day, are the real therapists; but strangely, they generally have no clear understanding of their lived practice. I have formed a kind of alliance with them; what I'm able to do is advance a theory of what they are doing, and this often provides strength and encouragement.'* (Kitwood, 1990, p. 42).

By claiming that people who provide the best dementia care were, whether or not they were aware of it, working as therapists, so Kitwood makes a number of arguments. First, he describes them as making the same type of imaginative leap that a psychotherapist does when they try to intuitively make sense of the meaning of an event to a client. At one point in the paper, he bemoans the lack of an attempt from researchers to enter into the lived experience of people with dementia – and in this area at least, the last 30 years have seen a substantial increase both in the amount of research and the value that is now placed on hearing the voice of people with dementia. Indeed, the importance of a collaborative approach between researchers and people with dementia is symbolized by the fact that the two series editors for this book are Dawn Brooker (a clinical psychologist and researcher) and Keith Oliver (an Alzheimer Society ambassador and expert by lived experience).

The second way in which Kitwood argues that the best dementia caregivers are also therapists is that there are parallels between a therapeutic relationship and that which develops in good dementia care. He states:

> '*I think, then, that our therapeutic response to a dementia sufferer often entails first responding non-verbally, to non-verbal signs (of distress, fear, loneliness, or whatever), and so making an emotional contact in which the verbal exchange is of very secondary importance. Remarkably, however, after we have established contact in this way, the words also begin to make sense. We need to slow down our thought processes, to become inwardly quiet, and to have a kind of poetic awareness: that is, to look for the significance of metaphor and allusion rather than pursuing meaning with a kind of relentless tunnel vision. The crucial issue is not that of adjusting the dementia sufferer to our everyday reality, but of adjusting ourselves, or "tuning in", to his or her emotional reality. When this happens, the meaning of apparently crazy remarks become crystal clear and sometimes we can give a voice to the dementia sufferer's experience; we are bringing it out, acknowledging it as real, and sometimes taking away its demonic force.*'
>
> Tom Kitwood, 1990, p 51.

In this regard, it is no coincidence that Kitwood's choice of 'person-centred' to describe his model of dementia care directly refers to the work of Carl Rogers – the doyen of humanistic counselling. The core therapeutic components of congruence, unconditional positive regard and empathy are central to both person-centred counselling and person-centred dementia care. For Kitwood, providing good dementia care means that people living with dementia should experience a sense of being understood, valued and emotionally contained. In this sense, the best dementia care workers may not be **doing** therapy, but they are **being** therapeutic by, in Kitwood's terms, combining validation, holding and facilitation (Kitwood, 1997; Kitwood and Brooker, 2019). From this perspective, as I discussed in Chapter 11, counselling principles are woven into the tapestry of care such that it helps the person who is living with dementia to make sense of their feelings (Stokes and Goudie, 1990). For Kitwood, then, every interaction with a person with even severe levels of cognitive impairment has the potential to be based on empathy – with care-workers enacting unconditional feelings of respect for the personhood of the individual (Cheston, 2019). The relationship that develops between a person with dementia and the best providers of dementia care is akin to the relationship between a therapist and a client: both can be construed as an '*I-thou*' rather than an '*I-it*' relationship (Swinton, 2017; Sabat, 2018). In an '*I-it*' relationship we relate to people with dementia as objects made up of specific, isolated components, and as separate and alien from us. An '*I-thou*' relationship by contrast is of one subject to another, with a dialogue that involves our whole being and recognizes the complexities of being a person – someone with a history and an interior world as well as a neurological impairment.

Importantly, adjusting to dementia involves addressing not just the changes in oneself that have already occurred but also the prospect of future changes. Adjusting to dementia involves grieving compounded by existential threat. The person may be aware of slips in the way they interact with others – of being embarrassed at failures of memory, and even ashamed of their own incompetence. One woman in a therapy group told the group, haltingly, shamefully, about how she had been playing with her young grandson on her knee – bouncing him up and down, when she realized that she could not remember his name. Through tears she said, '*What sort of grandmother am I, when I can't even remember my only grandson's name?*' Her forgetfulness made her un-like herself and dislike herself – she could no longer rely on herself to embody the attributes or characteristics that made her the person she took herself to be. At this point, a fellow group member took her hand and held it for the next few minutes. Gradually she came to herself again and thanked him. These small acts of kindness that occupy the therapeutic space allow people to reconcile themselves to the fact that while they are not the same person that they once were, nor are they entirely different. Instead, they are the same, but different.

Since I began this book with a quotation from Kitwood's 1990 paper entitled *Psychotherapy and dementia*, I thought it was fitting to end the book by reference to this neglected article:

'Thus, we are led to a more optimistic interpretation of dementia than that which has been generally adopted in recent years ... As yet, however, we are only on the edge of a truly personal understanding, and of a genuinely personal approach to the practicalities of care. A vast amount is known about the neurology and biochemistry of dementia, and for this we can be very thankful. But the crucial point is that no amount of scientific knowledge will ever add up to a personal and existential account; nor can scientific knowledge ever be a substitute ... Despite severe and frightening impairment, [the person living with dementia] can be enabled to be a person and to remain so until the point of death.'

Tom Kitwood, 1990, p 54–5.

Like Kitwood, I believe that psychotherapy, and psychotherapists, have an important role to play in enabling us all to remember that it is not the person with **dementia** who counts, but the **person** with dementia.

Summary of Part 4: Complicated psychotherapy

The type of neurological impairment and the extent to which it affects a person's cognitive abilities may mean that providing formal psychotherapeutic sessions may either not be possible (as is often the case for people with a diagnosis of bv-FTD), or that it needs to be delivered in a very different way. Where a client has a neurological impairment that affects their communication (such as a version of progressive primary aphasia) then it may be necessary to include a person who understands the context of their life to support the therapeutic process. Psychotherapeutic techniques also have an important role to play in the provision of care to people with severe levels of impairment. In particular, care staff need to be supported to make an imaginative leap into their patients' subjective experiences – similar to the empathic leap that characterizes psychotherapy. Additionally, using active listening skills and techniques from person-centred counselling should become routine parts of person-centred dementia care. This can help people with even very severe levels of dementia to connect with their emotional world, and thus provides a way of working through unmet needs which are associated with many challenging behaviours. Personal and social factors need to be fully assessed. These include aspects of the person's pre-morbid functioning, which may preclude therapy, such as narcissistic tendencies. People with dementia who are socially isolated, or who live within relationships that are characterized by malignant positioning may also not benefit from therapy – and in these cases other forms of intervention may be more appropriate.

Implications for people living with dementia

Many people living with dementia should think about the following points.

- Be aware that being in therapy is hard work. Psychotherapy places considerable demands on clients – especially when they are having to manage a cognitive impairment. But being in therapy is not impossible – and many people have found that it has been a great help.
- Ask the therapist to adapt the content of the sessions to make it more sustainable. This might involve practical changes to how therapy is organized (for instance having shorter sessions). It may also mean asking therapists to alter the way in which they ask questions or to provide summaries of what has been talked about.

Implications for family carers

People who are caring for someone with dementia should think about the following points.

- They should seek out therapeutic support if they are providing care for someone who has had a lifelong tendency to respond in a narcissistic fashion to challenges and threats.
- They should consider whether they may need to support the person they are caring for in therapy sessions, for instance by acting as a quasi-interpreter. This is especially likely to be the case if the person has been diagnosed with a primary progressive aphasia or as another neurological deficit that impairs their ability to communicate.

Implications for therapists

Healthcare professionals whose job involves offering specific counselling or psychotherapy sessions should think about the following points.

- They should assess the capacity of a person to adapt to their dementia before deciding whether, and if so, how to offer psychotherapy. This assessment needs to cover not only the level and nature of the person's cognitive impairment, but also the social and personal resources available to them.
- They should be prepared to include a partner or supporter in therapy if the person with dementia has severe problems in communicating, for instance if they have been diagnosed with a primary progressive aphasia. The final decision about this needs to rest with the person with dementia.
- Where the personal resources available to people are thin, as is the case for those people who habitually fall back on narcissistic defences, or if their social relationships are malignant or absent, then it may not be possible to work directly with the person.
- They should work indirectly with partners and families of someone with dementia where their underlying personality means that they are unable to engage in therapeutic work aimed at helping them to adjust. Where the person with dementia is emotionally fragile, then it is important to work with their main sources of support to build a sustainable narrative about how the person is coping, and how this relates to their life history.
- They should assess whether neurological impairments (whether these relate to a specific diagnosis such as bv-FTD or to the degree of cognitive impairment) mean that the person is unlikely to be unable to benefit from therapy.
- They should provide training to staff working in dementia care including how to use active listening and person-centred counselling skills such as resolution therapy as part of their day-to-day care.

Implications for dementia care workers

Staff working in dementia care should think about the following points.

- Recognize that good practice involves being psychotherapeutic.
- Seek out training and support, particularly around using person-centred counselling skills including resolution therapy.
- Be prepared to make an imaginative leap into the world of the people you work with, in which you empathically try to understand what the person is experiencing. At these times, you may attend less to what someone is saying and more to how they are saying it – in other words, listening to the emotional rather than to the factual meaning of what people say.
- Use non-verbal responses to build an emotional connection with the person that you are working with.

References

Aalten, P., Van Valen, E., Clare, L., Kenny, G., & Verhey, F. (2005). Awareness in dementia: a review of clinical correlates. *Aging & Mental Health, 9*(5), 414–422.

Aalten, P., Van Valen, E., De Vugt, M. E., Lousberg, R., Jolles, J., & Verhey, F. R. (2006). Awareness and behavioral problems in dementia patients: a prospective study. *International Psychogeriatrics, 18*(1), 3–17.

Aldridge, H., Fisher, P., & Laidlaw, K. (2019). Experiences of shame for people with dementia: an interpretative phenomenological analysis. *Dementia: the International Journal of Social Research and Policy, 18*(5), 1896–1911.

Alexander, C. M., Martyr, A., Gamble, L. D., Savage, S. A., Quinn, C., Morris, R. G., Collins, R. & Clare, L. (2021). Does awareness of condition help people with mild-to-moderate dementia to live well? Findings from the IDEAL programme. *BMC Geriatrics, 21*(1), 1–15.

Alexander, C.M., Martyr, A., & Clare, L. (2022). Changes in awareness of condition in people with mild-to-moderate dementia: longitudinal findings from the IDEAL cohort. *International Journal of Geriatric Psychiatry*, https://doi.org/10.1002/gps.5702 (accessed 1 July 2022).

Alnes, R., Kirkevold, M. & and Skovdahl, K. (2011a) Marte Meo counselling: a promising tool to support positive interactions between residents with dementia and nurses in nursing homes, *Journal of Research in Nursing, 16*(5), 415–433.

Alnes, R.E, Kirkevold, M. & and Skovdahl, K. (2011b) Insights gained through Marte Meo counselling: experiences of nurses in dementia specific care units. *International Journal of Older People Nursing 6*(2), 123–132.

Alzheimer's Research UK (2022a). Retrieved from https://www.dementiastatistics.org/statistics/impact-on-carers/ (accessed 1 July 2022).

Alzheimer's Research UK (2022b). Retrieved from https://www.dementiastatistics.org/statistics-about-dementia/ (accessed 1 July 2022).

Alzheimer's Society (2012). Are you worried about dementia? Retrieved from: https://yougov.co.uk/topics/lifestyle/articles-reports/2012/05/22/are-you-worried-about-dementia (accessed 1 July 2022).

Alzheimer's Society (2019). Retrieved from: https://www.alzheimers.org.uk/news/2019-05-15/lonely-future-120000-people-dementia-living-alone-set-double-next-20-years (accessed 1 July 2022).

Alzheimer's Society (2021). Retrieved from https://www.alzheimers.org.uk/sites/default/files/pdf/factsheet_risk_factors_for_dementia.pdf (accessed 1 July 2022).

APPG (All-Party Parliamentary Group) on Dementia (2013). *Dementia does not discriminate. The experience of black, Asian and minority ethnic communities.* London: Alzheimer's Society.

Babins, L. (1988). Conceptual analysis of validation therapy. *The International Journal of Aging and Human Development, 26*(3), 161–168.

Bachman, D. L., Wagner, M. T., DePalma, M., Spangengberg, K. B., Hendrix, S. A., & Perlman, D. J. (2000). Caregiver attitudes about patients told they have Alzheimer's disease after truth disclosure. *Journal of Clinical Geropsychology, 6*, 309–313.

Baghirathan, S., Cheston, R., Hui, R., Chacon, A., Shears, P. & Currie, K. (2020). A grounded theory analysis of the dementia experiences of people from three BME communities: balancing the need for support against fears of being diminished. *Dementia: the International Journal of Social Research and Policy, 19*(5), 1672–1691, https://doi.org/10.1177/1471301218804714 (accessed 1 July 2022).

Bahro, M., Silber, E., & Sunderland, T. (1995). How do patients with Alzheimer's disease cope with their illness? A clinical experience report. *Journal of American Geriatric Society, 93*, 291–296.

Balfour, A. (2006). Thinking about the experience of dementia: the importance of the unconscious. *Journal of Social Work Practice, 20*(3), 329–346.

Balfour, A. (2014). Developing therapeutic couple work in dementia care: The living together with dementia project. *Psychoanalytic Psychotherapy, 28*(3), 304–320. ISSN 0266-8734.

Balfour, A. (2020). The fragile thread of connection: living as a couple with dementia, in: S. Evans, J. Garner & R. Darnley-Smith (Eds.) *Psychodynamic Approaches to the Experience of Dementia*. London: Routledge.

Balfour, A. & Salter, L. (2018). Living together with dementia, in Andrew Balfour, Christopher Clulow and Kate Thompson (Eds.) *Engaging Couples: New Directions in Therapeutic Work with Families*, London: Routledge

Bamford, C., Lamont, S., Eccles, M., Robinson, L., May, C., & Bond, J. (2004). Disclosing a diagnosis of dementia: a systematic review. *International Journal of Geriatric Psychiatry, 19*(2), 151–169.

Bateman, A., & Fonagy, P. (2013). Mentalization-based treatment. *Psychoanalytic Inquiry, 33*(6), 595–613.

Beck, A.T. (1997). The past and future of cognitive therapy. *The Journal of Psychotherapy Practice and Research, 6*(4), 276.

Behuniak, S.M. (2011). The living dead? The construction of people with Alzheimer's disease as zombies. *Ageing & Society, 31*(1), 70–92.

Benbow, S. M., & Sharman, V. (2014). Review of family therapy and dementia: twenty-five years on. *International Psychogeriatrics, 26*(12), 2037–2050.

Bettelheim, B. (1976) *The Uses of Enchantment: The Meaning and Importance of Fairy Tales*. New York: Knopf.

Betts, N., & Cheston, R. (2011). From warding off to working through: helping people facing a diagnosis of dementia to change their relationship with their memory problems. *PSIGE Newsletter, 118*, 34–42.

Bielsten, T., & Hellström, I. (2019a). A review of couple-centred interventions in dementia: Exploring the what and why–Part A. *Dementia: the International Journal of Social Research and Policy, 18*(7–8), 2436–2449, https://doi.org/10.1177/1471301217737652 (accessed 1 July 2022).

Bielsten, T., & Hellström, I. (2019b). An extended review of couple-centred interventions in dementia: exploring the what and why—part B. *Dementia: the International Journal of Social Research and Policy, 18*(7–8), 2450–2473, https://doi.org/10.1177/1471301217737653 (accessed 1 July 2022).

Bird, M. (2001). Behavioural difficulties and cued recall of adaptive behaviour in dementia: experimental and clinical evidence. *Neuropsychological Rehabilitation, 11*(3–4), 357–375.

Blakemore, A., Kenning, C., Mirza, N., Daker-White, G., Panagioti, M., & Waheed, W. (2018). Dementia in UK South Asians: a scoping review of the literature, *British Medical Journal Open, 8*(4), e020290, https://doi.org/10.1136/bmjopen-2017-020290 (accessed 1 July 2022).

Bortolotti, L., & Widdows, H. (2011). The right not to know: the case of psychiatric disorders. *Journal of Medical Ethics, 37*(11), 673–676.

Bosson, J.K., Lakey, C.E., Campbell, W.K., Zeigler-Hill, V., Jordan, C.H., & Kernis, M.H. (2008). Untangling the links between narcissism and self-esteem: a theoretical and empirical review. *Social and Personality Psychology Compass, 2*(3), 1415–1439.

Bowlby, J. (1969). *Attachment and Loss, Vol. 1: Attachment.* London: Hogarth Press.

British Psychological Society Dementia Advisory Group (2016) *Psychological Dimensions of Dementia: Putting the Person at the Centre of Care.* Leicester: The British Psychological Society.

Brodaty, H., Gresham, M., & Luscombe, G. (1997). The Prince Henry Hospital dementia caregivers' training programme. *International Journal of Geriatric Psychiatry, 12*(2), 183–192.

Bryden, C. (2005). *Dancing with Dementia: My Story of Living Positively with Dementia.* London: Jessica Kingsley Publishers.

Burgener, S.C., Yang, Y., Gilbert, R., & Marsh-Yant, S. (2008). The effects of a multimodal intervention on outcomes of persons with early-stage dementia. *American Journal of Alzheimer's Disease and Other Dementias, 23*(4), 382–394.

Burke, B.L., Martens, A., & Faucher, E.H. (2010). Two decades of terror management theory: a meta-analysis of mortality salience research. *Personality and Social Psychology Review, 14*(2), 155–195.

Burns, A., Guthrie, E., Marino-Francis, F., Busby, C., Morris, J., Russell, E., Margison, F., Lennon, S. & Byrne, J. (2005). Brief psychotherapy in Alzheimer's disease: randomised controlled trial. *The British Journal of Psychiatry, 187*(2), 143–147.

Bush, T. (2003) Communicating with patients who have dementia. *Nursing Times 99*(48), 42–45.

Butler, T., & Fuhriman, A. (1983). Curative factors in group therapy: a review of the recent literature. *Small Group Behavior, 14*(2), 131–142.

Byszewski, A.M., Molnar, F.J., Aminzadeh, F., Eisner, M., Gardezi, F., & Bassett, R. (2007). Dementia diagnosis disclosure: a study of patient and caregiver perspectives. *Alzheimer Disease & Associated Disorders, 21*(2), 107–114.

Carreira, K., Miller, M.D., Frank, E., Houck, P.R., Morse, J.Q., Dew, M.A., Butters', M.A. & Reynolds III, C.F. (2008). A controlled evaluation of monthly maintenance interpersonal psychotherapy in late-life depression with varying levels of cognitive function. *International Journal of Geriatric Psychiatry, 23*(11), 1110–1113.

Chan, J., Churcher Clarke, A., Royan, L., Stott, J., & Spector, A. (2017). A mindfulness program manual for people with dementia. *Behavior Modification, 41*(6), 764–787, https://doi.org/10.1177/0145445517715872 (accessed 1 July 2022).

Chan, J., Leung, D.K., Walton, H., Wong, G.H., & Spector, A. (2020). Can mindfulness-based interventions benefit people with dementia? Drawing on the evidence from a systematic review in populations with cognitive impairments. *Expert Review of Neurotherapeutics, 20*(11), 1143–1156, https://doi.org/10.1080/14737175.2020.1810571 (accessed 1 July 2022).

Charlesworth, G., Sadek, S., Schepers, A., & Spector, A. (2015). Cognitive behavior therapy for anxiety in people with dementia: a clinician guideline for a person-centered approach. *Behavior Modification, 39*(3), 390–412, https://doi.org/10.1177/01454455 14561317 (accessed 1 July 2022).

Cheston, R. (1996) Stories and metaphors: talking about the past in a psychotherapy group for people with dementia. *Ageing and Society, 16*(5), 579–602.

Cheston, R. (1998). Psychotherapeutic work with people with dementia: a review of the literature. *British Journal of Medical Psychology, 71*(3), 211–231.

Cheston, R. (2005). Shame and avoidance: issues of remembering and forgetting with people with dementia. *Context: the Magazine for Family Therapy and Systemic Practice, 77*, 19–22.

Cheston, R. (2010). The fine art of living in the moment, in Jane Gilliard and Mary Marshall (Eds.) *Time for Dementia: A Collection of Writings on the Meaning of Time and Dementia*. Jessica Kingsley Press: London.

Cheston, R. (2013). Dementia as a problematic experience: using the Assimilation Model as a framework for psychotherapeutic work with people with dementia, *Neurodisability and Psychotherapy, 1*(1), 70–95.

Cheston, R. (2015). The role of the fear-of-loss-of-control marker within the accounts of people affected by dementia about their illness: implications for psychotherapy. *Quaderni di Psicoterapia Cognitiva, 37*, 45–66.

Cheston, R. (2019). Improving care: the next step forward – a commentary, in Dawn Brooker (Editor) and Tom Kitwood (2019). *Dementia Reconsidered, Revisited: The Person Still Comes First*. London: Open University Press.

Cheston, R. (2021) Working with narcissism in psychotherapy with people with dementia, in Christian E Salas, Oliver H Turnbull, Mark Solms (Eds.) *Clinical Studies in Neuropsychoanalysis Revisited* (pp. 207–221), London: Routledge. ISBN 9781032036878.

Cheston, R., & Bender, M. (1999) *Understanding Dementia: The Man with the Worried Eyes*. London: Jessica Kingsley Press.

Cheston, R., & Christopher, G. (2019). *Confronting the Existential Threat of Dementia: an Exploration into Emotion Regulation*. London: Springer.

Cheston, R., & Ivanecka, A. (2017). Individual and group psychotherapy with people affected by dementia: a systematic review of the literature. *International Journal of Geriatric Psychiatry, 32* (1), 3–31, https://doi.org/10.1002/gps.4529 (accessed 1 July 2022).

Cheston, R., Christopher, G. & Ismail, S. (2015). Dementia as an existential threat: the importance of self-esteem, social connectedness and meaning in life. *Science Progress*, 98(4), 416–419, https://doi.org/10.3184/003685015X14467423210693 (accessed 1 July 2022).

Cheston, R., Dodd, E., Christopher, G., Jones, C., Wildschut, T., & Sedikides, C. (2018a). Selective forgetting of self-threatening statements: mnemic neglect for dementia information in people with mild dementia. *International Journal of Geriatric Psychiatry, 33*(8), 1065–1073.

Cheston, R., Dodd, E., Christopher, G., Wildschut, T., & Sedikides, C. (2020). The mnemic neglect effect and information about dementia: age differences in recall. *Aging, Neuropsychology, and Cognition*, 1–13.

Cheston, R., Gatting, L., Marshall, A., Spreadbury, J. & Coleman, P. (2017). Markers of assimilation of problematic experiences in dementia within the LIVDEM project. *Dementia: The International Journal of Social Research and Policy, 16*(4), 443–460, https://doi.org/10.1177/1471301215602473 (accessed 1 July 2022).

Cheston, R., Jones, K., & Gilliard, J. (2003). Group psychotherapy and people with dementia. *Aging and Mental Health* 7(6): 452–461.

Cheston, R., Jones, K., & Gilliard, J. (2004). "Falling into a hole": narrative and emotional change in a psychotherapy group for people with dementia. *Dementia: The International Journal of Social Research and Policy, 3*(1), 95–103.

Cheston, R., Marshall, A., Jones, A., Spreadbury, J., & Coleman, P. (2018b). Living well with dementia groups: changes in participant and therapist verbal behaviour. *Aging and Mental Health, 22*(1), 61–69, https://doi.org/10.1080/13607863.2016.1231171 (accessed 1 July 2022).

Cheston, R., & Marshall A. (2019). *The Living Well with Dementia course – A Workbook for Facilitators*. London: Taylor-Francis.

Churcher Clarke, A., Chan, J.M.Y., Stott, J., Royan, L., & Spector, A. (2017). An adapted mindfulness intervention for people with dementia in care homes: feasibility pilot study. *International Journal of Geriatric Psychiatry, 32*(12), https://doi.org/10.1002/gps.4669 (accessed 1 July 2022).

Clare, L. (2002). We'll fight it as long as we can: coping with the onset of Alzheimer's disease. *Aging and Mental Health, 6*(2), 139–148.

Clare, L. (2003). Managing threats to self: awareness in early-stage Alzheimer's disease. *Social Science and Medicine, 57*(6), 1017–1029.

Clare, L., Quinn, C., Jones, I. R. & Woods R. T. (2016) "I don't think of it as an illness": illness representations in mild to moderate dementia. *Journal of Alzheimer's Disease, 51*(1), 139–150, https://doi.org/10.3233/JAD-150794 (accessed 1 July 2022).

Clare, L., Marková, I. S., Roth, I., & Morris, R. G. (2011). Awareness in Alzheimer's disease and associated dementias: theoretical framework and clinical implications. *Aging and Mental Health, 15*(8), 936–944.

Clare, L., Rowlands, J., Bruce, E., Surr, C., & Downs, M. (2008a). The experience of living with dementia in residential care: an interpretative phenomenological analysis. *The Gerontologist, 48*(6), 711–720.

Clare, L., Rowlands, J., Bruce, E., Surr, C., & Downs, M. (2008b). 'I don't do like I used to do': a grounded theory approach to conceptualising awareness in people with moderate to severe dementia living in long-term care. *Social Science & Medicine, 66*(11), 2366–2377.

Clare, L., Wilson, B. A., Carter, G., Roth, I., & Hodges, J. R. (2004). Awareness in early-stage Alzheimer's disease: relationship to outcome of cognitive rehabilitation. *Journal of Clinical and Experimental Neuropsychology, 26*(2), 215–226.

Clare, L., & Wilson, B. (2006). Longitudinal assessment of awareness in early-stage Alzheimer's disease using comparable questionnaire-based and performance based measures: A prospective one-year follow-up study. *Aging and Mental Health, 10*(2), 156–165.

Clarke, P.B., Adams, J. K., Wilkerson, J. R., & Shaw, E. G. (2016). Wellness-based counselling for caregivers of persons with dementia. *Journal of Mental Health Counselling, 38*(3), 263–277.

Cohen-Mansfield, J. (1997). Conceptualization of agitation: results based on the Cohen-Mansfield agitation inventory and the agitation behavior mapping instrument. *International Psychogeriatrics, 8*(S3), 309–315.

Collins, R.N., Gilligan, L. J., & Poz, R. (2018). The evaluation of a compassion-focused therapy group for couples experiencing a dementia diagnosis. *Clinical Gerontologist, 41*(5), 474–486.

Cotter, V. T., Gonzalez, E. W., Fisher, K., & Richards, K. C. (2018). Influence of hope, social support, and self-esteem in early-stage dementia. *Dementia: The International Journal of Social Research and Policy, 17*(2), 214–224, https://doi.org/10.1177/1471301217741744 (accessed 1 July 2022).

Craig, C., Hiskey, S., Royan, L., Poz, R., & Spector, A. (2018). Compassion focused therapy for people with dementia: a feasibility study. *International Journal of Geriatric Psychiatry, 33*(12), 1727–1735, https://doi.org/10.1002/gps.4977 (accessed 1 July 2022).

Davenhill, R. (2007). *Looking into Later Life: A Psychoanalytic Approach to Depression and Dementia in Old Age.* London: Karnac Books.

Department of Health. (2013). *Dementia – A State of the Nation Report on Dementia and Care and Support in England.* Available at: https://www.gov.uk/government/uploads/system/uploads/attachment_data/file/262139/Dementia.pdf (accessed 1 July 2022).

Deponte, A., & Missan, R. (2007). Effectiveness of validation therapy (VT) in group: preliminary results. *Archives of Gerontology and Geriatrics, 44*(2), 113–117.

Derksen, E., Vernooij-Dassen, M., Scheltens, P., & Olde-Rikkert, M. (2006). A model for disclosure of the diagnosis of dementia. *Dementia: The International Journal of Social Research and Policy, 5*(3), 462–468.

Di Pierro, R., Mattavelli, S., & Gallucci, M. (2016). Narcissistic traits and explicit self-esteem: The moderating role of implicit self-view. *Frontiers in Psychology, 7*, 1815.

Dimaggio, G., Semerari, A., Falcone, M., Nicolò, G., Carcione, A., & Procacci, M. (2002). Metacognition, states of mind, cognitive biases and interpersonal cycles. Proposal for an integrated narcissism model. *Journal of Psychotherapy Integration, 12*(4), 421–451.

Dodd, E., Ismail S., Christopher G., Wildschut R. T., Sedikides C., & Cheston R. (2022) Nostalgic conversations: the co-production of an intervention package for people living with dementia and their spouse. *Dementia: The International Journal of Social Research and Policy, 21*(2), 489–502, https://doi.org/10.1177/14713012211047350 (accessed 1 July 2022).

Douglas, S., Stott, J., Spector, A., Brede, J., Hanratty, É., Charlesworth, G., Noone, D., Payne, J., Patel, M. & Aguirre, E. (2021). Mindfulness-based cognitive therapy for depression in people with dementia: a qualitative study on participant, carer and facilitator experiences. *Dementia: The International Journal of Social Research and Policy, 21*(2), 457–476, https://doi.org/10.1177/14713012211046150 (accessed 1 July 2022).

Duran-Kiraç, G., Uysal-Bozkir, Ö., Uittenbroek, R., van Hout, H., & Broese van Groenou, M.I. (2021). Accessibility of health care experienced by persons with dementia from ethnic minority groups and formal and informal caregivers: a scoping review of European literature. *Dementia: The International Journal of Social Research and Policy, 21*(2), 677–700.

Ebert, A. R., Kulibert, D., & McFadden, S. H. (2020). Effects of dementia knowledge and dementia fear on comfort with people having dementia: Implications for dementia-friendly communities. *Dementia: The International Journal of Social Research and Policy, 19*(8), 2542–2554, https://doi.org/10.1177/1471301219827708 (accessed 1 July 2022).

Edwards, H.B., Whiting, P.,, Ijaz, S., Leach, V., Richards, A., Cullum, S., Cheston, R., & Savović, J. (2018). Quality of family relationships and outcomes of dementia: a systematic review. *BMJ Open, 8*(1), http://dx.doi.org/10.1136/bmjopen-2016-015538 (accessed 1 July 2022).

Evans, N., Cheston, R. & Harris, N. (2015). Personal message cards: an evaluation of an alternative method of delivering Simulated Presence Therapy. *Dementia: The International Journal of Social Research and Policy, 15*(6), 1703–1715. https://doi.org/10.1177/1471301215574363 (accessed 1 July 2022).

Evans, S. (2008). 'Beyond forgetfulness': how psychoanalytic ideas can help us to understand the experience of patients with dementia. *Psychoanalytic Psychotherapy, 22*(3), 155–176.

Evans, S. (2019). A psychoanalytic and philosophical exploration of boredom and disengagement in dementia, in S. Evans, J. Garner, & R.D. Smith, (Eds.) *Psychodynamic Approaches to the Experience of Dementia* (pp. 186–198). London: Routledge.

Evans, S., Garner, J., & Smith, R. D. (Eds.) (2019). *Psychodynamic Approaches to the Experience of Dementia: Perspectives from Observation, Theory and Practice.* London: Routledge.

Farina, F. R., Bennett, M., Griffith, J. W., & Lenaert, B. (2020). Fear of memory loss predicts increased memory failures and lower quality of life in older adults: preliminary findings from a fear-avoidance of memory loss (FAM) scale. *Aging and Mental*

Health, 26(3), 486–492, https://doi.org/10.1080/13607863.2020.1856780 (accessed 1 July 2022).

Feeney, J.A., & Noller, P. (1990). Attachment style as a predictor of adult romantic relationships. *Journal of Personality and Social Psychology, 58*(2), 281.

Feil, N. (1993). *The Validation Breakthrough: Simple Techniques for Communicating with People with "Alzheimer's-type Dementia"*. Pennsylvania: Health Professions Press.

Feil, N. (1996). *The Validation Breakthrough. Techniques for Communicating with People with Alzheimer's-type Dementia*. Pennsylvania: Health Professions Press.

Fonagy, P., & Bateman, A. W. (2006). Mechanisms of change in mentalization-based treatment of BPD. *Journal of Clinical Psychology, 62*(4), 411–430.

Fratiglioni, L., Marseglia, A., & Dekhtyar, S. (2020). Ageing without dementia: can stimulating psychosocial and lifestyle experiences make a difference? *The Lancet Neurology, 19*(6), 533–543, https://doi.org/10.1016/S1474-4422(20)30039-9 (accessed 1 July 2022).

Gergen, K. J., & Kaye, J. (1992). Beyond narrative in the negotiation of therapeutic meaning, in S. McNamee & K. J. Gergen (Eds.), *Therapy As Social Construction* (pp. 166–185). New York: Sage Publications, Inc.

Gilbert, P. (1997). The evolution of social attractiveness and its role in shame, humiliation, guilt and therapy. *British Journal of Medical Psychology, 70*(2), 113–147.

Gilbert, P. (2009a). *The Compassionate Mind: A New Approach to the Challenges of Life*. London: Constable and Robinson.

Gilbert, P. (2009b). Introducing compassion-focused therapy. *Advances in Psychiatric Treatment, 15*(3), 199–208.

Gilbert, P. (2014a). Body shame: A biopsychosocial conceptualisation and overview with treatment implications, in Paul Gilbert (Ed.) *Body Shame* (pp. 17–68). Routledge: London.

Gilbert, P. (2014b). The origins and nature of compassion focused therapy. *British Journal of Clinical Psychology, 53*(1), 6–41.

Gilbert, P., & Woodyatt, L. (2017). An evolutionary approach to shame-based self-criticism, self-forgiveness, and compassion, in *Handbook of the Psychology of Self-Forgiveness* (pp. 29–41). Cham: Springer.

Goffman, E. (1963). *Stigma: Notes on the Management of Spoiled Identity*. New Jersey: Prentice Hall.

Goodwin, B., & Waters, H. (2009). 'In solitary confinement': planning end-of-life well-being with people with advanced dementia, their family and professional carers. *Mortality, 14*(3), 265–285.

Green, J. D., Sedikides, C., Pinter, B., & Van Tongeren, D. R. (2009). Two sides to self-protection: self-improvement strivings and feedback from close relationships eliminate mnemic neglect. *Self and Identity, 8*(2–3), 233–250.

Griffiths, A. W., Shoesmith, E., Sass, C., Nicholson, P., & Charura, D. (2021). Relational counselling as a psychosocial intervention for dementia: qualitative evidence from people living with dementia and family members. *Dementia, 20*(6), 2091–2108.

Grossman, P., Niemann, L., Schmidt, S., & Walach, H. (2004). Mindfulness-based stress reduction and health benefits: a meta-analysis. *Journal of Psychosomatic Research, 57*(1), 35–43.

Gudex, C., Horsted, C., & Hill, L. (2008). Marte Meo used in nursing homes. *Danish Journal of Nursing 108*(18): 52–58.

Gutstein, S. E. & Sheely, R. K. (2002). *Relationship Development Intervention with Young Children: Social and Emotional Development Activities for Asperger Syndrome, Autism, PDD, and NDL* (Vol. 2). London: Jessica Kingsley Publishers.

Hailstone, J., Mukadam, N., Owen, T., Cooper, C., & Livingston, G. (2017). The development of attitudes of people from ethnic minorities to help-seeking for dementia (APEND): a questionnaire to measure attitudes to help-seeking for dementia in people from south Asian backgrounds in the UK. *International Journal of Geriatric Psychiatry, 32*(3), 288–296, https://doi.org/10.1002/gps.4462 (accessed 1 July 2022).

Henry, H. M., Stiles, W. B., & Biran, M. W. (2005). Loss and mourning in immigration: using the assimilation model to assess continuing bonds with native culture. *Counselling Psychology Quarterly, 18*(2), 109–119.

Henry, H. M., Stiles, W. B., Biran, M. W., Mosher, J. K., Brinegar, M. G., & Banerjee, P. (2009). Immigrants' continuing bonds with their native culture: assimilation analysis of three interviews. *Transcultural Psychiatry, 46*(2), 257–284.

Hermans, H. J., Kempen, H. J., & Van Loon, R. J. (1992). The dialogical self: beyond individualism and rationalism. *American Psychologist, 47*(1), 23.

Hoffman, L. (2001). *Family Therapy: An Intimate History*. New York: Norton.

Holst, G., & Hallberg, I. R. (2003). Exploring the meaning of everyday life, for those suffering from dementia. *American Journal of Alzheimer's Disease & Other Dementias, 18*(6), 359–365.

Honos-Webb, L., Lani, J.A., & Stiles, W.B. (1999). Discovering markers of assimilation stages: the fear of losing control marker. *Journal of Clinical Psychology, 55*, 1441–1452.

Honos-Webb, L., & Stiles, W. B. (1998). Reformulation of assimilation analysis in terms of voices. *Psychotherapy: Theory, Research, Practice, Training, 35*(1), 23.

Honos-Webb, L., Stiles, W., Greenberg, L., & Goldman, R. (1998). Assimilation analysis of process-experiential psychotherapy: a comparison of two cases. *Psychotherapy Research, 8*(3), 264–286.

Horowitz, M. J. (1989). Clinical phenomenology of narcissistic pathology. *Psychiatric Clinic of North America, 12*, 531–539.

Hughes, J., & Cheston, R. (2021). Psychotherapy in old age: ethical issues, in Manuel Trachsel, Serife Tekin, Nikola Biller-Adorno, Jens Gaab and John Sadler (Eds.), *The Oxford Handbook of Psychotherapy Ethics*. Oxford: Oxford University Press, DOI: 10.1093/oxfordhb/9780198817338.013.66.

Husband, H. J. (2000). Diagnostic disclosure in dementia: an opportunity for intervention? *International Journal of Geriatric Psychiatry, 15*(6), 544–547.

Hyun, J., Hall, C. B., Sliwinski, M. J., Katz, M. J., Wang, C., Ezzati, A., & Lipton, R. B. (2020). Effect of mentally challenging occupations on incident dementia differs between African Americans and non-Hispanic Whites. *Journal of Alzheimer's Disease, 75*(4), 1405–1416.

Ismail, S. U. (2017). *Nostalgia as a psychological resource for people with dementia*. Doctoral dissertation, University of the West of England.

Ismail, S., Christopher, G., Dodd, E., Wildschut, T., Sedikides, C., Ingram, T., Jones, R., Noonan, K., Tingley, D. & Cheston, R. (2018). Psychological and mnemonic benefits of nostalgia for people with dementia. *Journal of Alzheimer's Disease, 65*(4), 1327–1344, https://doi.org/10.3233/JAD-180075.

Ismail, S., Dodd, E., Christopher, G., Wildschut, T., Sedikides, C., & Cheston, R. (2022). The content of nostalgic memories among people living with dementia. *The International Journal of Aging and Human Development, 94*(4), 436–458, https://doi.org/10.1177/00914150211024185 (accessed 1 July 2022).

Jackman, L., & Beatty, A. (2015). Using the Newcastle Model to understand people whose behaviour challenges in dementia care. *Nursing Older People, 27*(2).

James, I.A., & Jackman, L. (2017). *Understanding Behaviour in Dementia That Challenges: A Guide to Assessment and Treatment*. London: Jessica Kingsley Publishers.

James, I. A., Mackenzie, L., & Mukaetova-Ladinska, E. (2006). Doll use in care homes for people with dementia. *International Journal of Geriatric Psychiatry: A Journal of the Psychiatry of Late Life and Allied Sciences, 21*(11), 1093–1098.

Kabat-Zinn, J. (2013). *Full Catastrophe Living, Revised Edition: How to Cope with Stress, Pain and Illness using Mindfulness Meditation.* London: Hachette.

Kernberg, O. (1975). *Borderline Conditions and Pathological Narcissism.* New York: Jason Aronson.

Kiosses, D. N., Areán, P. A., Teri, L., & Alexopoulous, G. S. (2010). Home-delivered problem adaptation therapy (PATH) for depressed, cognitively impaired, disabled elders: a preliminary study. *American Journal of Geriatric Psychiatry, 18*, 988–998.

Kiosses, D. N., Ravdin, L. D., Gross, J., Raue, P., Kotbi, N. & Alexopoulous, G. S. (2015). Problem adaptation therapy for older adults with major depression and cognitive impairment: a randomised clinical trial. *JAMA Psychiatry, 72*, 22–30.

Kiosses, D. N., Teri, L., Velligan, D. I. & Alexopoulos, G. S. (2011). A home-delivered intervention for depressed, cognitively impaired disabled elders. *International Journal of Geriatric Psychiatry, 26*, 256–262.

Kitwood, T. (1990) Psychotherapy and dementia. *Newsletter of the Psychotherapy Section of the British Psychological Society, 8*, 40–56.

Kitwood, T. M. (1997). *Dementia reconsidered: The Person Comes First.* Buckingham: Open University Press.

Kitwood, T. & Brooker, D. (Eds.) (2019). *Dementia Reconsidered, Revisited: The Person Still Comes First.* London: Open University Press.

Kokkonen, T-M., Cheston, R., Dallos, R., & Smart, C. (2014). Attachment and coping of dementia care staff: the role of staff attachment style, geriatric nursing self-efficacy, and approaches to dementia in burnout. *Dementia: the International Journal of Social Research and Policy, 13*(4), 544–568, https://doi.org/10.1177/1471301213479469 (accessed 1 July 2022).

Kurz, A., Thöne-Otto, A., Cramer, B., Egert, S., Frölich, L., Gertz, H. J., Kehl, V., Wagenpfeil, S. & Werheid, K. (2012). CORDIAL: cognitive rehabilitation and cognitive-behavioral treatment for early dementia in Alzheimer disease: a multi-center, randomized, controlled trial. *Alzheimer Disease & Associated Disorders, 26*(3), 246–253.

La Fontaine, J., Ahuja, J., Bradbury, N. M., Phillips, S., & Oyebode, J. R. (2007). Understanding dementia amongst people in minority ethnic and cultural groups. *Journal of Advanced Nursing, 60*(6), 605–614.

Lee, G. J., Do, C., & Suhr, J. A. (2020). Effects of personal dementia exposure on subjective memory concerns and dementia worry. *Aging, Neuropsychology, and Cognition, 28*(6), 855–870, https://doi.org/10.1080/13825585.2020.1836119 (accessed 1 July 2022).

Link, B. G. (1987) Understanding labelling effects in the area of mental disorders: an assessment of the effects of expectations of rejection. *American Sociological Review, 52*, 96–112.

Link, B., Cullen, F., Struening, E., Shrout, P., & Dohrenwend, B. (1989) A modified labelling theory approach to mental disorders: an empirical assessment. *American Sociological Review, 54*, 400–423.

Link, B. G. & Phelan, J. C. (2001) Conceptualizing stigma. *Annual Review of Sociology, 27*, 363–385.

Lishman, E., Cheston, R., & Smithson, J. (2016), The paradox of dementia: meaning making before and after receiving a diagnosis of dementia. *Dementia: The International Journal of Social Research and Policy, 15*(2), 181–203, https://doi.org/10.1177/1471301214520781 (accessed 1 July 2022).

Logsdon, R. G., McCurry, S. M., & Teri, L. (2007). Time-limited support groups for individuals with early-stage dementia and their care partners: preliminary outcomes from a controlled clinical trial. *Clinical Gerontologist, 30*(2), 5–19.

Logsdon, R. G., Pike, K. C., McCurry, S. M., Hunter, P., Maher, J., Snyder, L., & Teri, L. (2010). Early-stage memory loss support groups: outcomes from a randomized controlled clinical trial. *Journals of Gerontology Series B: Psychological Sciences and Social Sciences, 65*(6), 691–697.

Loi, S.M., Tsoukra, P., Chen, Z., Wibawa, P., Mijuskovic, T., Eratne, D., Di Biase, M.A., Evans, A., Farrand, S., Kelso, W. and Goh, A.M, Walterfang M. & Velakoulis, D. (2021). Mortality in dementia is predicted by older age of onset and cognitive presentation. *Australian & New Zealand Journal of Psychiatry*, https://doi.org/10.1177/00048674211041003 (accessed 1 July 2022).

MacLeod, S., Musich, S., Hawkins, K., Alsgaard, K., & Wicker, E. R. (2016). The impact of resilience among older adults. *Geriatric Nursing, 37*(4), 266–272.

Magai, C., & Cohen, C. I. (1998). Attachment style and emotion regulation in dementia patients and their relation to caregiver burden. *The Journals of Gerontology Series B: Psychological Sciences and Social Sciences, 53*(3), 147–154.

Mair, M. (2013). *Between Psychology and Psychotherapy (Psychology Revivals): A Poetics of Experience*. London: Routledge.

Marshall, A., Spreadbury, J., Cheston, R., Coleman, P., Ballinger, C., Mullee, M., Pritchard, J., Russell, C., & Bartlett, E. (2015). A pilot randomised control trial to compare changes in quality of life for participants with early diagnosis dementia who attend a "Living Well with Dementia" group compared to waiting list control. *Aging and Mental Health, 19*(6), 526–535, doi: 10.1080/13607863.2014.954527.

Marzanski, M. (2000). Would you like to know what is wrong with you? On telling the truth to patients with dementia. *Journal of Medical Ethics, 26*(2), 108–113.

Maurer, K., Volk, S., & Gerbaldo, H. (1997). Auguste D and Alzheimer's disease. *The Lancet, 349*(9064), 1546–1549.

McBride, K. (2008). *Will I Ever Be Good Enough? Healing the Daughters of Narcissistic Mothers*. New York: Simon and Schuster.

McKillop, J. (2003). *Opening Shutters – Opening Minds*. Dementia Services Dementia Centre, Stirling: University of Stirling.

Miesen, B. (1992). Attachment theory and dementia. *Caregiving in Dementia. Research and applications, 1*, 38–56.

Miesen, B. (2016). *Dementia in Close-Up*. London: Routledge.

Mittelman, M. S., Haley, W. E., Clay, O. J., & Roth, D. L. (2006). Improving caregiver wellbeing delays nursing home placement of patients with Alzheimer's disease. *Neurology, 67*, 1592–1599.

Moniz-Cook, E., Stokes, G., & Agar, S. (2003). Difficult behaviour and dementia in nursing homes: five cases of psychosocial intervention. *Clinical Psychology & Psychotherapy: An International Journal of Theory & Practice, 10*(3), 197–208.

Morton, I. (1999). *Person-centred Approaches to Dementia Care*. London: Speechmark Press.

Morton, I. (2017). Building therapeutic relationships with people who have dementia, in Graham Stokes and Fiona Goudie (Eds.) *The Essential Dementia Care Handbook* (pp. 174–180). London: Routledge.

Mosak, H. H. (2014). *Ha, Ha and Aha: The Role of Humour in Psychotherapy*. Hoboken: Taylor and Francis..

Mukadam, N., Cooper, C. & Livingston, G. (2011). A systematic review of ethnicity and pathways to care in dementia. *International Journal of Geriatric Psychiatry, 26*(1), 12–20.

Neal, M., & Wright, P. B. (2003). Validation therapy for dementia. *Cochrane Database of Systematic Reviews, 3,* https://doi.org/10.1002/14651858.CD001394 (accessed 1 July 2022).

Newman, D. W., & Beail, N. (2002). Monitoring change in psychotherapy with people with intellectual disabilities: the application of the assimilation of problematic experiences scale. *Journal of Applied Research in Intellectual Disabilities, 15*(1), 48–60.

Norton, M. C., Piercy, K. W., Rabins, P. V., Green, R. C., Breitner, J. C., Østbye, T., Corcoran, C., Welsh-Bohmer, K. A., Lyketsos, C. G. & Tschanz, J. T. (2009). Caregiver–recipient closeness and symptom progression in Alzheimer Disease. The Cache County dementia progression study. *Journals of Gerontology Series B: Psychological Sciences and Social Sciences, 64*(5), 560–568.

Oliver, K. (2019). *Dear Alzheimer's: A Diary of Living with Dementia.* London: Jessica Kingsley Publishers.

Oliver, K., O'Malley, M., Parkes, J., Stamou, V., La Fontaine, J., Oyebode, J., & Carter, J. (2020). Living with young onset dementia and actively shaping dementia research – The Angela Project. *Dementia: The International Journal of Social Research and Policy, 19*(1), 41–48.

Osatuke, K., & Stiles, W.B. (2006). Problematic internal voices in clients with borderline features: An elaboration of the assimilation model. *Journal of Constructivist Psychology, 19*(4), 287–319.

Parveen, S., Peltier, C., & Oyebode, J. R. (2017). Perceptions of dementia and use of services in minority ethnic communities: a scoping exercise. *Health & Social Care, 25*(2), 734–742.

Perren, S., Schmid, R., Herrmann, S., & Wettstein, A. (2007). The impact of attachment on dementia-related problem behavior and spousal caregivers' well-being. *Attachment & Human Development, 9*(2), 163–178.

Phung, K. T., Waldorff, F. B., Buss, D. V., Eckermann, A., Keiding, N., Rishøj, S., Siersma, V., Sørensen, J., Søgaard, R., Sørensen, L.V. & Waldemar, G. (2013). A three-year follow-up on the efficacy of psychosocial interventions for patients with mild dementia and their caregivers: the multicentre, rater-blinded, randomised Danish Alzheimer Intervention Study (DAISY). *BMJ Open, 3*(11), e003584.

Pinner, G., & Bouman, W. P. (2003). Attitudes of patients with mild dementia and their carers towards disclosure of the diagnosis. *International Psychogeriatrics, 15*(3), 279–288.

Pratchett, T. (2015). Retrieved from an interview published in the Guardian newspaper https://www.theguardian.com/books/2015/mar/15/a-butt-of-my-own-jokes-terry-pratchett-on-the-disease-that-finally-claimed-him (accessed 1 July 2022).

Pratt, R. & Wilkinson, H. (2003) A psychosocial model of understanding the experience of receiving a diagnosis of dementia, *Dementia: the International Journal of Social Research and Policy,* 2 (2), 181–199.

Pyszczynski, T., Solomon, S., & Greenberg, J. (2015). Thirty years of terror management theory: from genesis to revelation, in *Advances in Experimental Social Psychology* (Vol. 52, pp. 1–70). Academic Press.

Quinn, C., Clare, L., & Woods, B. (2009). The impact of the quality of relationship on the experiences and wellbeing of caregivers of people with dementia: a systematic review. *Aging and Mental Health, 13*(2), 143–154.

Quintana-Hernandez, D. J., Miro-Barrachina, M. T., Ibáñez-Fernández, I. J., Pino, A. S. D., Quintana-Montesdeoca, M. P., Rodriguez-de Vera, B., Morales-Casanova, D., Pérez-Vieitez, M. D. C., Rodriguez-Garcia, J. & Bravo-Caraduje, N. (2016). Mindfulness in the maintenance of cognitive capacities in Alzheimer's disease: a randomized clinical trial. *Journal of Alzheimer's Disease, 50*(1), 217–232.

Rabinowitz, J., Davidson, M., De Deyn, P. P., Katz, I., Brodaty, H., & Cohen-Mansfield, J. (2005). Factor analysis of the Cohen-Mansfield Agitation Inventory in three large samples of nursing home patients with dementia and behavioral disturbance. *The American Journal of Geriatric Psychiatry, 13*(11), 991–998.

Retzinger, S. M. (1991). Shame, anger, and conflict: case study of emotional violence. *Journal of Family Violence, 6*(1), 37–59.

Retzinger, S. M. (1995). Identifying shame and anger in discourse. *American Behavioral Scientist, 38*(8), 1104–1113.

Rivera-Hernandez, M., Kumar, A., Epstein-Lubow, G., & Thomas, K. S. (2019). Disparities in nursing home use and quality among African American, Hispanic, and White Medicare residents with Alzheimer's disease and related dementias. *Journal of Aging and Health, 31*(7), 1259–1277.

Roberts, J. P. (1982). Foulkes' concept of the matrix. *Group Analysis, 15*(2), 111–126.

Robinson, L., Clare, L., & Evans, K. (2005). Making sense of dementia and adjusting to loss: psychological reactions to a diagnosis of dementia in couples. *Aging and Mental Health, 9*(4), 337–347.

Robinson, L., Gemski, A., Abley, C., Bond, J., Keady, J., Campbell, S., Samsi, K., & Manthorpe, J. (2011). The transition to dementia–individual and family experiences of receiving a diagnosis: a review. *International Psychogeriatrics, 23*(7), 1026–1043.

Rosow, K., Holzapfel, A., Karlawish, J. H., Baumgart, M., Bain, L. J. & Khachaturian, A. S. (2011). Countrywide strategic plans on Alzheimer's disease: developing the framework for the international battle against Alzheimer's disease. *Alzheimer's and Dementia, 7,* 615–621, https://doi.org/10.1016/j.jalz.2011.09.226 (accessed 1 July 2022).

Routledge, C., Wildschut, T., Sedikides, C., & Juhl, J. (2013). Nostalgia as a resource for psychological health and well-being. *Social and Personality Psychology Compass, 7*(11), 808–818.

Sabat, S. R. (2002). Surviving manifestations of selfhood in Alzheimer's disease: a case study. *Dementia: The International Journal of Social Research and Policy, 1*(1), 25–36.

Sabat, S. R. (2018). *Alzheimer's Disease and Dementia: What Everyone Needs to Know.* Oxford: Oxford University Press.

Sabat, S. R., Napolitano, L., & Fath, H. (2004). Barriers to the construction of a valued social identity: a case study of Alzheimer's disease. *American Journal of Alzheimer's Disease & Other Dementias, 19*(3), 177–185.

Salzman, C., Jeste, D. V., Meyer, R. E., Cohen-Mansfield, J., Cummings, J., Grossberg, G. T., Jarvik, L., Kraemer, H. C., Lebowitz, B. D., Maslow, K., Pollock, B. G., Rashkind M., Schultz, S., Wang, P., Zito, J. M., & Zubenko, G. S. (2008). Elderly patients with dementia-related symptoms of severe agitation and aggression: consensus statement on treatment options, clinical trials methodology, and policy. *The Journal of Clinical Psychiatry, 69*(6), 889–898.

Scholey, K. A., & Woods, B. T. (2003). A series of brief cognitive therapy interventions with people experiencing both dementia and depression: a description of techniques and common themes. *Clinical Psychology & Psychotherapy: An International Journal of Theory & Practice, 10*(3), 175–185.

Sedikides, C., & Wildschut, T. (2018). Finding meaning in nostalgia. *Review of General Psychology, 22*(1), 48–61. https://doi.org/10.1037/gpr0000109 (accessed 1 July 2022).

Sedikides, C., & Wildschut, T. (2019). The sociality of personal and collective nostalgia. *European Review of Social Psychology, 30*(1), 123–173.

Sedikides, C., Green, J. D., Saunders, J., Skowronski, J. J., & Zengel, B. (2016). Mnemic neglect: Selective amnesia of one's faults. *European Review of Social Psychology, 27*(1), 1–62.

Segal, Z. V., Williams, M., & Teasdale, J. (2018). *Mindfulness-based cognitive therapy for depression*. New York: Guilford Publications.

Shoesmith, E., Griffiths, A. W., Sass, C., & Charura, D. (2020). Effectiveness of counselling and psychotherapeutic interventions for people with dementia and their families: a systematic review. *Ageing & Society*, 1–28.

Simpson, J. A., & Rholes, W. S. (2017). Adult attachment, stress, and romantic relationships. *Current Opinion in Psychology, 13*, 19–24.

Sinason, V. (1992). *Mental Handicap and the Human Condition: New Approaches From the Tavistock.* London. Free Associations. Books.

Smith, A., King, E., Hindley, N., Barnetson, L., Barton, J., & Jobst, K. A. (1998). The experience of research participation and the value of diagnosis in dementia: implications for practice. *Journal of Mental Health, 7*(3), 309–321.

Snow, K., Cheston, R. & Smart, C. (2015). 'Making sense' of dementia: exploring the use of the MAPED to understand how couples process a dementia diagnosis. *Dementia: the International Journal of Social Research and Policy, 15*(6), 1515–1533, https://doi.org/10.1177/1471301214564447 (accessed 1 July 2022).

Snyder, L., Jenkins, C., & Joosten, L. (2007). Effectiveness of support groups for people with mild to moderate Alzheimer's disease: an evaluative survey. *American Journal of Alzheimer's Disease and Other Dementia, 22*(1), 14–19.

Snyder, L., Quayhagen, M.P., Shepherd, S., & Bower, D. (1995). Supportive seminar groups: an intervention for early-stage dementia patients. *Gerontologist 35*, 691–695.

Solomon, S., Greenberg, J., & Pyszczynski, T. (1991). A terror management theory of social behavior: the psychological functions of self-esteem and cultural worldviews. *Advances in Experimental Social Psychology, 24*, 93–159.

Solomon, S., Greenberg, J., & Pyszczynski, T. (2015). *The Worm at the Core: On the Role of Death in Life*. New York: Random House.

Spector, A., Charlesworth, G., King, M., Lattimer, M., Sadek, S., Marston, L., Rehill, A., Hoe, J., Qazi, A., Knapp, M. & Orrell, M. (2015). Cognitive-behavioural therapy for anxiety in dementia: pilot randomised controlled trial. *The British Journal of Psychiatry, 206*(6), 509–516, https://doi.org/10.1192/bjp.bp.113.140087 (accessed 1 July 2022).

Stanley, M. A., Calleo, J., Bush, A. L., Wilson, N., Snow, A. L., Kraus-Schuman, C., Paukert, A. L., Petersen, N. J., Brenes, G.A., Schulz, P. E., & Williams, S. P. (2013). The Peaceful Mind Program: a pilot test of a cognitive-behavioral therapy-based intervention for anxious patients with dementia. *The American Journal of Geriatric Psychiatry, 21*(7), 696–708.

Stephens, A., Cheston, R., & Gleeson, K. (2013). An exploration into the relationships people with dementia have with physical objects: an ethnographic study. *Dementia: The International Journal of Social Research and Policy, 12*(6), 697–712.

Stiles, W. B. (2001). Assimilation of problematic experiences. *Psychotherapy: Theory, Research, Practice, Training, 38*(4), 462.

Stiles, W. B., Honos-Webb, L., & Lani, J. A. (1999). Some functions of narrative in the assimilation of problematic experiences. *Journal of Clinical Psychology, 55*(10), 1213–1226.

Stiles, W. B., Meshot, C., Anderson, T., & Sloan, W. (1992). Assimilation of problematic experiences: the case of John Jones. *Psychotherapy Research, 2*(2), 81–101.

Stokes, G. (2017). *Challenging Behaviour in Dementia: A Person-centred Approach*. London: Routledge.

Stokes, G. & Goudie, F. (1989). Understanding confusion. *Nursing Times, 85*(39), 35–37.

Stokes, G. & Goudie, F. (Eds.) (1990). *Working with Dementia*. Oxon: Winslow Press.

Sukhawathanakul, P., Crizzle, A., Tuokko, H., Naglie, G., & Rapoport, M. J. (2021). Psychotherapeutic interventions for dementia: a systematic review. *Canadian Geriatrics Journal*, *24*(3), 222, https://doi.org/10.5770/cgj.24.447 (accessed 1 July 2022).

Swaffer, K. (2016). *What the Hell Happened to my Brain? Living Beyond Dementia.* Jessica Kingsley Publishers: London.

Swinton, J. (2017). *Dementia: Living in the Memories of God.* London: Scm Press.

Teri, L. & Gallagher-Thompson, D. (1991). Cognitive-behavioural intervention for treatment of depression in Alzheimer's patients. *Gerontologist*, 31, 413–416.

Toseland, R. W., Diehl, M., Freeman, K., Manzanares, T., Naleppa, M., & McCallion, P. (1997). The impact of validation group therapy on nursing home residents with dementia. *Journal of Applied Gerontology*, *16*(1), 31–50.

Tuerk, R., & Sauer, J. (2015). Dementia in a Black and minority ethnic population: characteristics of presentation to an inner London memory service. *British Journal of Psychiatry Bulletin*, *39*, 162–166.

United Nations (2022). Retrieved from https://www.un.org/en/global-issues/ageing (accessed 1 July 2022).

van Wijngaarden, E., Alma, M. & The, A-M. (2019). 'The eyes of others' are what really matters: The experience of living with dementia from an insider perspective. *PloS One*, *14*(4), https://doi.org/10.1371/journal.pone.0214724 (accessed 1 July 2022).

Varvin, S., & Stiles, W. (1999). Emergence of severe traumatic experiences: an assimilation analysis of psychoanalytic therapy with a political refugee. *Psychotherapy Research*, *9*(3), 381–404.

Waldorff, F. B., Buss, D.V., Eckermann, A., Rasmussen, M. L. H., Keiding, N., Rishòj, S., Siersma, V., Sòrensen, J., Sòrensen, LV., Vogel, A. & Waldemar, G. (2012). Efficacy of psychosocial intervention in patients with mild Alzheimer's disease: the multicentre, rater blinded, randomised Danish Alzheimer Intervention Study (DAISY). *British Medical Journal*, *345*:e4693, https://doi.org/10.1136/bmj.e4693 (accessed 1 July 2022).

Watkins, B., Cheston, R., Jones, K. & Gilliard, J. (2006). "Coming out with Alzheimer's disease": changes in insight during a psychotherapy group for people with dementia. *Aging and Mental Health*, *10*(2), 1–11.

Watts S., Cheston R., Moniz-Cook E., Burley C. & Guss R. (2014). Post-diagnostic support for people living with dementia, in R Guss et al. (on behalf of the Faculty of the Psychology of Older People, and in collaboration of people living with dementia and the Dementia Workstream Expert Reference Group) *Clinical Psychology in the Early Stage Dementia Care Pathway*. London: British Psychological Society.

Weaks, D., Johansen, R., Wilkinson, H., & McLeod, J. (2009). *There is Much More to My Practice Than Checking Up on Tablets. Developing Nursing Practice: A Counselling Approach to Delivering Post-Diagnostic Dementia Support.* Edinburgh: University of Edinburgh.

Wildschut, T., & Sedikides, C. (2020). The psychology of nostalgia: delineating the emotion's nature and functions, in M. H. Jacobson (Ed.), *Nostalgia now: Cross-disciplinary perspectives on the past in the present*. London: Routledge Press.

Wildschut, T., Sedikides, C., Arndt, J., & Routledge, C. (2006). Nostalgia: content, triggers, functions. *Journal of Personality and Social Psychology*, *91*(5), 975.

Wilson, J. (2011). The assimilation of problematic experiences sequence: an approach to evidence-based practice in bereavement counselling. *Journal of Social Work in End-of-Life & Palliative Care*, *7*(4), 350–362.

Wilson, J. F., Gabriel, L., & Stiles, W. B. (2021). Assimilation in bereavement: charting the process of grief recovery in the case of Sophie. *British Journal of Guidance & Counselling*, 1–14.

Windle, G. (2011). What is resilience? A review and concept analysis. *Reviews in Clinical Gerontology*, *21*(2), 152–169.

Winter, B. (2020). *Exploring the Relationship of Couples Living with Dementia and the Role of Couples Therapy: A Thematic Analysis*. Doctoral dissertation, University of the West of England, Bristol.

Wolverson, E. L., Clarke, C., & Moniz-Cook, E. (2010). Remaining hopeful in early-stage dementia: a qualitative study. *Aging & Mental Health*, *14*(4), 450–460.

Wong, Y., & Tsai, J. (2007). Cultural models of shame and guilt. *The self-conscious emotions: Theory and Research*, *209*, 223.

World Alzheimer Report (2012). *Overcoming the Stigma of Dementia*. London: Alzheimer's Disease International (ADI).

Wright, L. K. (1994). Alzheimer's disease afflicted spouses who remain at home: can human dialectics explain the findings? *Social Science & Medicine*, *38*(8), 1037–1046.

Wright, L. K., Hickey, J. V., Buckwalter, K. C., & Clipp, E. C. (1995). Human development in the context of aging and chronic illness: the role of attachment in Alzheimer's disease and stroke. *The International Journal of Aging and Human Development*, *41*(2), 133–150.

Yale, R. (1995). *Developing Support Groups for Individuals with Early-Stage Alzheimer's Disease*. The Maple Press Company: York, PA.

Yalom, I. D. (2008). *Staring at the sun: Overcoming the dread of death*. New York: Little, Brown Book Group.

Yalom, I. D., & Leszcz, M., (2020). *The theory and practice of group psychotherapy*. London: Hachette.

Young, J. E., & Flanagan, C. (1998). Schema-focused therapy for narcissistic patients, in E. F. Ronninggstam (Ed.), *Disorders of Narcissism: Diagnostic, Clinical, and Empirical Implications*. New York: American Psychiatric Press.

Author index

Subject index